# Science 2
## Student Guide

Part 1

**K12**
A Stride Company

At Stride, Inc. (NYSE: LRN) – formerly K12 Inc. – we are reimagining lifelong learning as a rich, deeply personal experience that prepares learners for tomorrow. Since its inception, Stride has been committed to removing barriers that impact academic equity and to providing high-quality education for anyone—particularly those in underserved communities. The company has transformed the teaching and learning experience for millions of people by providing innovative, high-quality, tech-enabled education solutions, curriculum, and programs directly to students, schools, the military, and enterprises in primary, secondary, and post-secondary settings. Stride is a premier provider of K–12 education for students, schools, and districts, including career learning services through middle and high school curriculum. Providing a solution to the widening skills gap in the workplace and student loan crisis, Stride equips students with real world skills for in-demand jobs with career learning. For adult learners, Stride delivers professional skills training in healthcare and technology, as well as staffing and talent development for Fortune 500 companies. Stride has delivered millions of courses over the past decade and serves learners in all 50 states and more than 100 countries. The company is a proud sponsor of the Future of School, a nonprofit organization dedicated to closing the gap between the pace of technology and the pace of change in education. More information can be found at stridelearning.com, K12.com, destinationsacademy.com, galvanize.com, techelevator.com, and medcerts.com.

978-1-60153-332-6

Printed by Bradford & Bigelow, Newburyport, MA, USA, May 2021.

# Table of Contents

# *Student Guide*
## Lesson 1: Meet the Metrics

- Measure length, mass, weight, temperature, and liquid volume using a metric ruler, a balance, a spring scale, a thermometer, and a graduated cylinder, then express those measurements in standard metric units of centimeters, grams, newtons, degrees Celsius, and milliliters.
- Distinguish the difference between mass and weight.
- Recognize some common equivalencies within the metric system, such as 1000 milliliters in 1 liter, 100 centimeters in 1 meter, and 1000 grams in 1 kilogram.
- Identify the boiling and freezing points of water and the average body temperature in degrees Celsius and compare them to points on the Fahrenheit scale.
- Use the scientific method to ask questions, make hypotheses, collect data, analyze results, and formulate conclusions.

## Lesson Objectives

- Identify some common tools used by scientists for measuring, such as a balance, a graduated cylinder, a metric ruler, and a thermometer.
- Identify four common metric units of measurement: centimeters, grams, mililiters, and degrees Celsius.
- Explore concepts to be addressed during the year in Science 2.

---

# PREPARE

Approximate lesson time is 60 minutes.

## Advance Preparation

- It's important that you read the Course Introduction for Science 2 before your student begins the course. You can find the course introduction at the beginning of the Meet the Metrics lesson.
- It's important that you read the course introduction for Science 2nd Grade before starting this lesson. You can find it by clicking the OLS "Help" section.
- If you don't already have them, you will need a metric ruler and Celsius thermometer (not mercury or digital) for this unit.
- Create Metric Shuffle Cards for this Science lesson. Cut out the measurement terms and tool names from the Metric Shuffle Cards sheet. For easier sorting and handling, glue them to index cards or card stock.

---

## Materials

For the Student

    balance, primary

    cylinders, graduated

    cubes, centimeter/gram (6)

    ruler, metric

    thermometer - Celsius

    💻 Measuring Mania

    pencils, no. 2

    💻 Metric Shuffle Cards

Optional

    card stock

    index cards, 4" x 6" (15)

    balance, primary  - two-pan

## Keywords and Pronunciation

**length** : The distance from one end of something to the other end. A football field has a *length* of about 91 meters.

**length** : The distance from one end of something to the other end. A football field has a *length* of about 91 metres.

**mass** : The amount of matter in an object. The *mass* of an object is the same on Earth as it is on the moon.

**temperature** : A measure of how hot or cold something is. The *temperature* in the desert is often very high.

**volume** : The amount of space an object takes up. Large objects have more volume than small objects.

---

# LEARN

## Activity 1: Welcome to Science 2 *(Online)*

## Activity 2: Scientific Tools *(Online)*

## Activity 3: Speaking the Same Language *(Online)*

## Activity 4: Measuring Mania *(Online)*

## Activity 5: The Metric Shuffle *(Online)*

## Activity 6. Optional: What Would You Use? *(Online)*

# ASSESS

## Lesson Assessment: Meet the Metrics (*Online*)

Your learning coach will help you complete an offline assessment covering the main objectives of this lesson. Your learning coach will score this assessment.

---

# LEARN

## Activity 7. Optional: Measure and Bake (*Online*)

## Name _____        Date _____

## Measuring Mania

Write each measurement. Remember to include units.

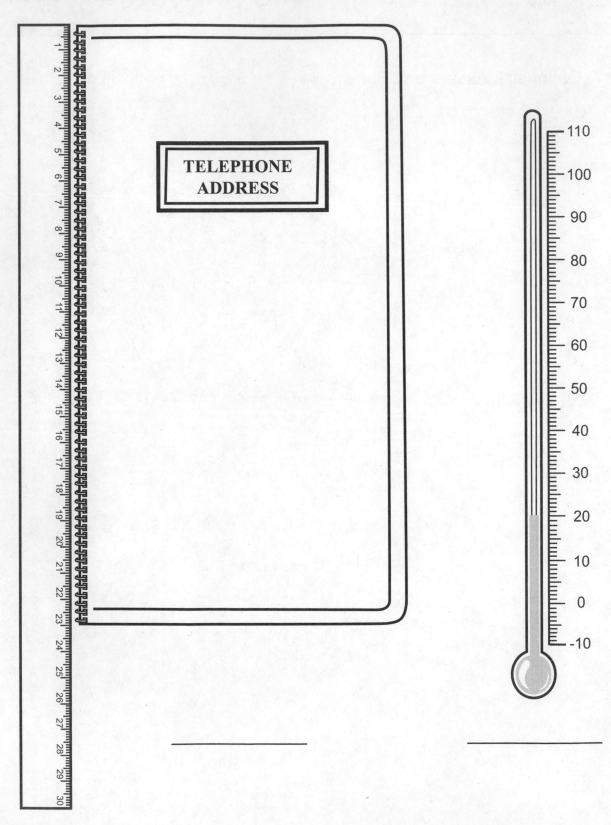

Name _____          Date _____

# Measuring Mania

Write each measurement. Remember to include units.

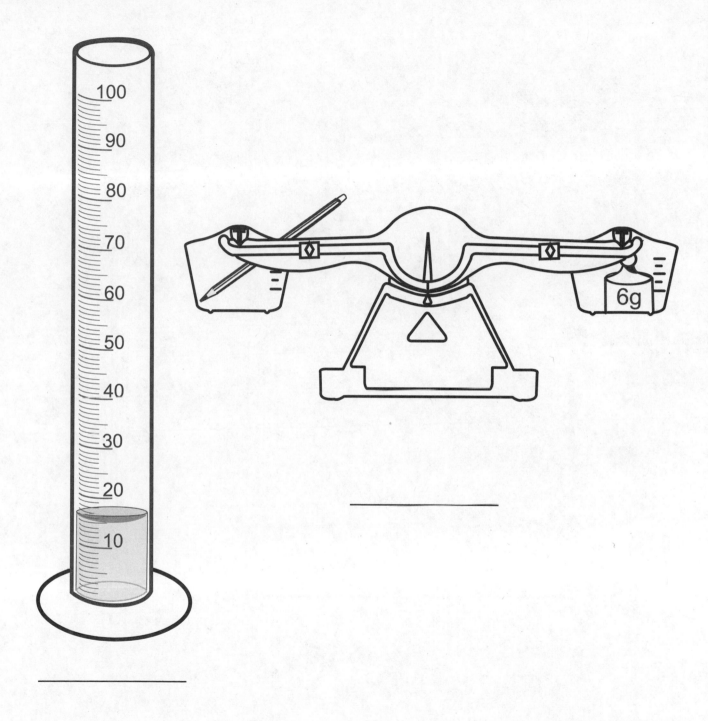

# Metric Shuffle Cards

Cut

| balance | thermometer |
| graduated cylinder | metric ruler |
| temperature | mass |

# Metric Shuffle Cards

Cut

| | |
|---|---|
| volume | length |
| milliliter | gram |
| degrees Celsius | centimeter |

# Lesson Assessment

## *Meet the Metrics*

**For question 1 you will need the following materials: balance, graduated cylinder, thermometer, metric ruler.**

**1.** Name each of these four scientific tools.

**2.** Which tool would you use to measure the mass of a baseball?

**3.** Which tool would you use to measure the metric length of a table?

**4.** What units of metric measurement are on a thermometer?

**5.** What units of metric measurement are on a balance?

**6.** What unit of metric measurement do we use to measure volume?

# Student Guide
## Lesson 2: Why Does a Meter Matter?

### Lesson Objectives

- Know that 100 centimeters equal 1 meter.
- Know that 1000 millimeters equal 1 meter.
- Know that meters, centimeters, and millimeters are units of length.

# PREPARE

Approximate lesson time is 60 minutes.

### Advance Preparation

- If you don't already have it, you will need a meter stick (100 cm) for this lesson.

### Materials

For the Student

    meter stick, 100 cm

    ruler, metric

    🖳 Why Does a Meter Matter?

    book - phone

    rice - dry, 1 grain

    penny

    table

Optional

    ball

    markers, colored, 8 or more

    string - one yard

### Keywords and Pronunciation

**centimeter** : A common metric unit of length. There are 100 *centimeters* in a meter.

**meter** : The basic unit of length in the metric system. A *meter* is a little longer than a yard.

**millimeter** : A small metric unit of length. There are 1000 *millimeters* in a meter.

# LEARN
## Activity 1: Taking Measurements *(Online)*

## Activity 2: Meters, Centimeters, and Millimeters (Online)

## Activity 3: Why Does a Meter Matter? (Online)

**Safety**

Accompany your student when he goes outside. Never leave him unattended outdoors.

## Activity 4. Optional: Meters Matter (Online)

---

# ASSESS

## Lesson Assessment: Why Does a Meter Matter (Online)

Your learning coach will help you complete an offline assessment covering the main objectives of this lesson. Your learning coach will score this assessment.

---

# LEARN

## Activity 5. Optional: Measuring Irregular Objects (Online)

---

Name _____     Date _____

# Why Does a Meter Matter?

| | | |
|---|---|---|
| Pillow | _____ cm | |
| Phone book | _____ cm | |
| Height of table | _____ cm | |
| Car | _____ m | _____ m _____ cm |
| Length of room | _____ m | _____ m _____ cm |
| Grain of rice | _____ mm | _____ cm |
| Penny | _____ mm | _____ cm |

10 millimeters (mm) = 1 centimeter (cm)      100 centimeters (cm) = 1 meter (m)
1,000 millimeters (mm) = 1 meter

metric ruler
meter stick
meters (**m**)
centimeters (**cm**)
millimeters (**mm**)

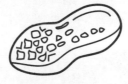

metric ruler
meter stick
meters (**m**)
centimeters (**cm**)
millimeters (**mm**)

metric ruler
meter stick
meters (**m**)
centimeters (**cm**)
millimeters (**mm**)

## Lesson Assessment

# *Why Does a Meter Matter?*

1. What is the standard unit of length in the metric system?

2. How many centimeters are in a meter?

3. How many millimeters are in a meter?

4. If an object is shorter than a meter, what other units can you use to measure it?

5. What tool would you use to measure the length of a horse?

# Student Guide
## Lesson 3: Temperature Scales

In this lesson, your student will learn about temperature scales. First, he will compare different types of scales to the metric system scales. Next, your student will discover how a scientist invented a scale for measuring temperature. Last, he will perform Gabriel Fahrenheit's experiment to create his own thermometer.

### Lesson Objectives
- Measure temperatures on the Celsius scale.
- Identify the boiling point of water, the freezing point of water, and the average body temperature.
- Compare temperatures on the Fahrenheit and Celsius scales.
- Create a temperature scale.

# PREPARE

Approximate lesson time is 60 minutes.

### Materials
> For the Student
>> pencils, no. 2
>> paper, 8 1/2" x 11"
>> 🖳 Testing Temperature
>> pencils, colored, 16 or more
>> 🖳 Benchmark Temperature Lab Sheet
>> cups, plastic (3)
>> salt - 2 tablespoons
>> thermometer tube, unmarked
>> tubs, margarine
>> ice cubes - 1 cup
>> ruler, metric
>> thermometer - Celsius
>> water - room temperature
>> water - warm tap
> Optional
>> 🖳 Temperature Scales Cards
>> index cards, 4" x 6"

## Keywords and Pronunciation

**scale** : A series of marks or points at known intervals used to measure something in specific units. A thermometer uses a type of scale.

**Celsius** (SEL-see-uhs) : The unit of temperature measurement in the metric measuring system. When the air temperature is 0 degrees Celsius, water will freeze.

**degree** : The unit used for measuring temperature. Water will boil at 100 degrees Celsius.

**Fahrenheit** (FAIR-uhn-hiyt) : The unit of temperature measurement in the U.S. Customary measuring system. If the air temperature is 100 degrees Fahrenheit, it is a very hot day!

**thermometer** : An instrument that measures temperature. A thermometer tells you how hot or cold something is.

---

# LEARN
## Activity 1: Rate Your Favorite Foods *(Online)*

## Activity 2: Testing Temperature *(Online)*

## Activity 3: Make Your Own Temperature Scale *(Online)*
### Safety
Use warm, not boiling or scalding, water.

Never place a thermometer in boiling water unless the thermometer's scale measures more than 100 degrees Celsius.

Do not use a mercury thermometer for Science lessons. Caution your student to be careful when handling the thermometer. The glass at the bulb is very thin and could break.

## Activity 4. Optional: Compare Fahrenheit and Celsius *(Online)*

---

# ASSESS

## Lesson Assessment: Temperature Scales (*Online*)
Your learning coach will help you complete an offline assessment covering the main objectives of this lesson. Your learning coach will score this assessment.

---

# LEARN
## Activity 5. Optional: Weather Temperature *(Online)*

---

Name _____          Date _____

# Benchmark Temperature Lab Sheet

Write the temperature of each according to your temperature scale and the Celsius scale. Use the table at the bottom of this sheet to record the degrees Fahrenheit. Round to the nearest ten when necessary. Safety Reminder: Do not place the laboratory thermometer in your mouth.

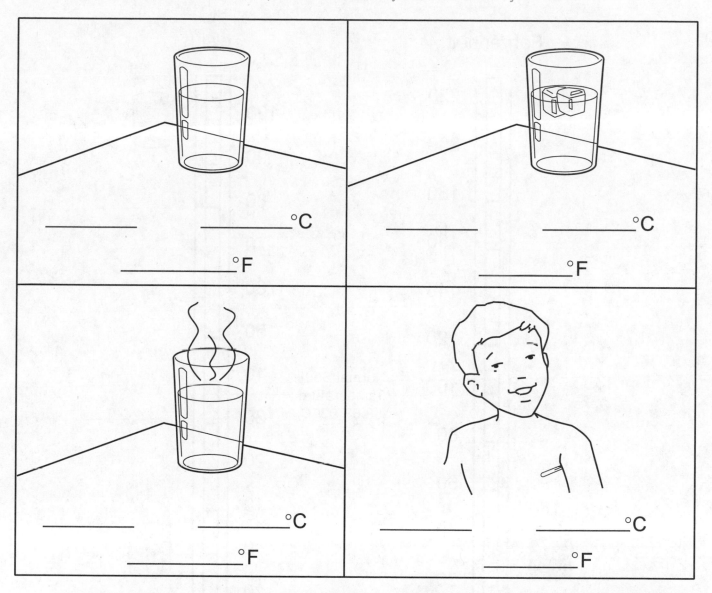

| Fahrenheit | 32 | 50 | 68 | 86 | 104 | 122 | 140 | 158 | 176 | 194 | 212 |
|---|---|---|---|---|---|---|---|---|---|---|---|
| Celsius | 0 | 10 | 20 | 30 | 40 | 50 | 60 | 70 | 80 | 90 | 100 |

Name _____          Date _____

# Testing Temperature Activity Sheet

Color each thermometer to the point of body temperature. Draw a line across each thermometer at the freezing point and boiling point of water on both scales. Remember that each scale is different!

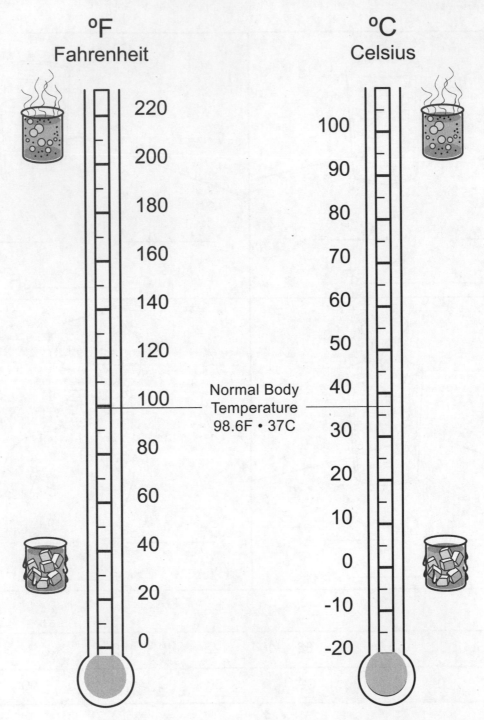

°F
Fahrenheit

°C
Celsius

Normal Body
Temperature
98.6F • 37C

Name _____          Date _____

## Temperature Scales Cards

<table>
<tr><td>32° F</td><td>212° F</td><td>98.6° F</td></tr>
<tr><td>0° C</td><td>100° C</td><td>37° C</td></tr>
</table>

Answers: ice: 32°F, 0°C    boiling water: 212° F, 100°C    body temperature: 98.6°F, 37°C

# Lesson Assessment

## *Temperature Scales*

**1.** What do the lines on a thermometer show?

**2.** Which temperature scale has a freezing point of 0?

**3.** On the Celsius scale, what is the boiling point of water?

**4.** At what temperature does water freeze on the Celsius scale and on the Fahrenheit scale?

**5.** What is the normal human body temperature in degrees Celsius?

# Student Guide
## Lesson 4: Let's Use a Liter

### Lesson Objectives
- Recognize that there are 1000mL in a liter.
- Measure volume in milliliters using a graduated cylinder.

---

# PREPARE

Approximate lesson time is 60 minutes.

### Advance Preparation
- For this Science lesson, gather three flavors and colors of powdered drink mix (or use three different colors of fruit drink). Add water to the powdered mixes and put them in three easy-to-pour cups marked "Secret Ingredient 1," "Secret Ingredient 2," and "Secret Ingredient 3." Mark the empty cup "Special Formula." Make more of each drink than you need, in case of spills or mismeasurement.

- If you do not wish to have your student drink the juice, you can use water instead.

### Materials
    For the Student
        container, plastic 1 liter
        water
        💻 Read a Liter
        cylinders, graduated - 250 mL
        cup - measuring
        water - 150 milliliters
        💻 The Secret Formula
        cups, plastic (4)
        drink mix, powdered - 3 varieties
    Optional
        eyedropper
        funnel
        💻 How Much Is a Liter?
        pencils, no. 2
        💻 Measuring a Solid
        cylinders, graduated
        rocks - small (3)

---

**Keywords and Pronunciation**

liter : The basic metric unit of volume. A liter is made up of smaller units called milliliters.

meniscus (muh-NIS-kuhs) : The curved surface of a liquid in a container. The bottom of the meniscus of the water in a graduated cylinder shows the volume of the water.

milliliter : A metric unit of volume. There are 1000 milliliters in 1 liter.

volume : The amount of space an object takes up. Large objects have more volume than small objects.

---

# LEARN
## Activity 1: What Is Volume? *(Online)*

## Activity 2: Measuring with Liters *(Online)*

## Activity 3: Looking at Liters *(Online)*

## Activity 4: The Secret Formula *(Online)*
### Safety
This activity involves eating or using food. Before beginning, check with your doctor, if necessary, to assess whether your student will have any allergic reaction to this food.

## Activity 5: How Much Is a Liter? *(Online)*

## Activity 6. Optional: Measuring Volume *(Online)*

---

# ASSESS

## Lesson Assessment: Let's Use a Liter (*Online*)
Your learning coach will help you complete an offline assessment covering the main objectives of this lesson. Your learning coach will score this assessment.

---

# LEARN
## Activity 7. Optional: Measuring a Solid *(Online)*

---

**Name**       **Date**

# The Secret Formula

Follow the directions written below.

Put one tablespoon of a powered drink in #1. Put one tablespoon of a different colored powered drink in #2. Put one tablespoon of another different colored powered drink in #3.

Pour 200 mL of water into each cup.
Measure 100 mL of secret ingredient #1.
Pour it into cup #4.
What color is the liquid in cup #4?

Measure 36 mL of secret ingredient # 2.
Pour it into cup #4.
What color is the liquid in cup #4?

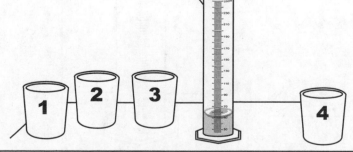

Measure 50 mL of secret ingredient #3.
Pour it into cup #4.
What color is the liquid in cup #4?

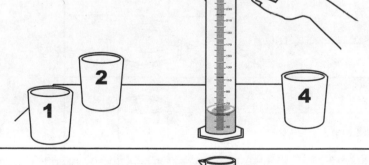

How many mL are in each cup?
You may now drink the Secret Formula.
Prepare for super thinking powers!

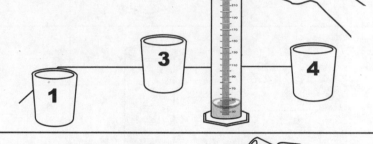

2S01-04M

## Name

## Date

# Read a Liter

Write how many mL of liquid are in each graduated cylinder.

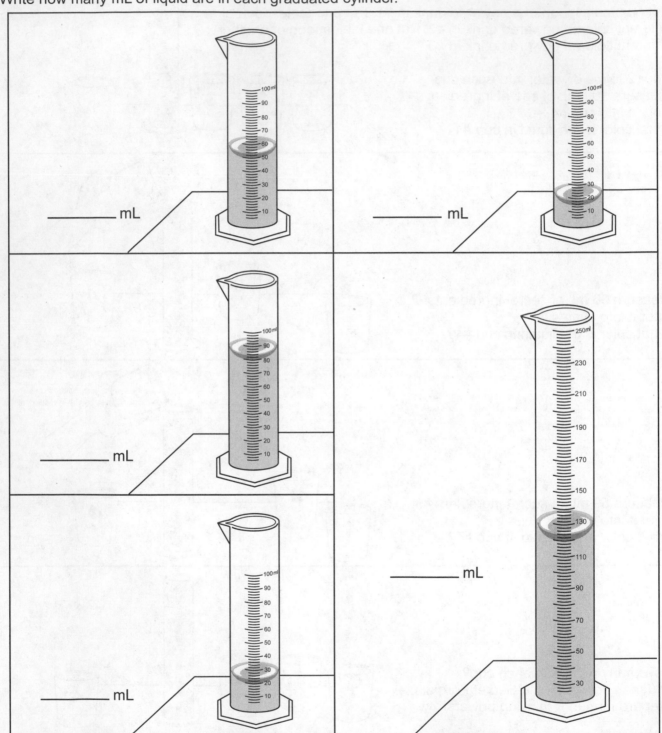

_____ mL

_____ mL

_____ mL

_____ mL

_____ mL

Name _____          Date _____

# How Much Is a Liter?

Prediction: How many milliliters do you think it will take to fill the one-liter bottle? _____

Use tally marks to show many times you filled the graduated cylinder with 100 mL _____

How many times did you fill the graduated cylinder? _____

How many milliliters are in the one-liter bottle? _____

Name _____    Date _____

# Measuring a Solid

Fill the graduated cylinder to 50 ml.
Tilt the graduated cylinder to the side and add a rock.
Read the volume after the rock is added.
Record your answers in the correct places on the chart.
Subtract the bottom number from the top number to find the volume of the rock.
Repeat these directions for the other rocks.


Volume after adding the rock    _____ mL

Volume before adding the rock ____50____ mL

Volume of the rock                 _____ mL



Volume after adding the rock    _____ mL

Volume before adding the rock ____50____ mL

Volume of the rock                 _____ mL



Volume after adding the rock    _____ mL

Volume before adding the rock ____50____ mL

Volume of the rock                 _____ mL

# Lesson Assessment

## *Let's Use a Liter*

1. What tool do scientists use to measure liquid volume?

2. How many milliliters are in 1 liter?

3. What does a graduated cylinder measure?

# Student Guide
## Lesson 5: The Scientific Method

### Lesson Objectives

- Identify the steps in the scientific method.

---

# PREPARE

Approximate lesson time is 60 minutes.

### Materials

For the Student

    🖳 Bouncing Balls Lab Sheet

    ball, rubber (2)

    crayons, 16 or more

    pencils, no. 2

    chair

Optional

    meter stick, 100 cm

    🖳 The Scientific Method Crossword Puzzle

    🖳 Salty Water Lab Sheet

    glasses, drinking - clear (2)

    salt

    spoon

    water - hot

    water - ice

### Keywords and Pronunciation

**conclusion** : The result of an experiment, based on the data. The conclusion tells others what happened in an experiment.

**data** (DAY-tuh) : All of the information collected from an experiment. After an experiment, the *data* show what happened.

**hypothesis** (hiy-PAH-thuh-sis) : A possible explanation of something you observed. Your *hypothesis* tries to explain what you observed.

**observation** : Something you notice by using your senses. Seeing, hearing, tasting, touching, and smelling are all ways of making an *observation*.

**procedure** : A way of doing something in steps. To follow a *procedure* carefully, you must do each step.

---

# LEARN
## Activity 1: Following the Rules (Online)

## Activity 2: Bouncing Balls (Online)
**Safety**

Help your student when he stands on the chair so he doesn't fall.

## Activity 3. Optional: The Scientific Method Crossword Puzzle (Online)

---

# ASSESS
## Lesson Assessment: The Scientific Method (Online)
Your learning coach will help you complete an offline assessment covering the main objectives of this lesson. Your learning coach will score this assessment.

---

# LEARN
## Activity 4: Salty Water (Online)

Name _____        Date _____

## Bouncing Balls Lab Sheet

Question:

_____

Hypothesis:

I think the _____ ball will bounce the highest because

_____

Materials:

Procedure:

1. Climb on a chair with the two balls to be tested.

Name _____            Date _____

## Bouncing Balls Lab Sheet: Part Two

Observations:

|        | Trial 1 | Trial 2 | Trial 3 | Trial 4 | Trial 5 |
|--------|---------|---------|---------|---------|---------|
| Ball 1 |         |         |         |         |         |
| Ball 2 |         |         |         |         |         |

Conclusion:

Which ball bounced the highest?

Is this the ball you thought would be the bounciest?

Why do you think this ball bounced the highest?

Which ball would you take to your friend's house to play with?

Name _____ Date _____

# The Scientific Method Crossword Puzzle

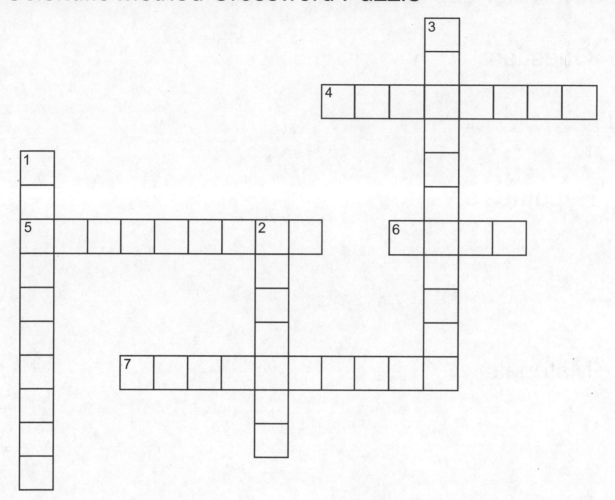

**DOWN:**

1. A possible explanation based on known information.

2. Everything that happened in the experiment.

3. Something noticed by watching very carefully during the experiment.

**ACROSS:**

4. The scientific method begins with this.

5. A way of doing the experiment step by step.

6. All the information collected from an experiment.

7. At the end of the experiment, you use all the information to make a _____.

---

WORD BANK

**conclusion    data    hypothesis    observation    question    results    procedure**

---

Name _____ Date _____

## Salty Water Lab Sheet

Question:

Hypothesis:

Materials:

Procedure:
1.

Name _____          Date _____

## Salty Water Lab Sheet

Observations:

| | SPOONS OF SALT |
|---|---|
| HOT | |
| COLD | |

Conclusion:

Did the hot water or the cold water dissolve more salt?


Was your hypothesis correct?


Why do you think more salt dissolved in this water?

# Lesson Assessment

## *The Scientific Method*

**1.** What is the first step in the scientific method?

**2.** What is a hypothesis?

**3.** What is the name for the information you write down after you observe an experiment?

# Student Guide
## Lesson 6: Let's Measure Mass

### Lesson Objectives

- Know that there are 1,000 grams in a kilogram.
- Measure mass, in grams, using a double-pan balance.
- Interpret results on a bar graph.
- Record results on a bar graph.

---

# PREPARE

Approximate lesson time is 60 minutes.

### Advance Preparation

- For this Science lesson you will need five different-sized pebbles or rocks and marshmallows. Measure the mass of the pebbles and choose those that weigh 100 grams or less. Paint them gold or yellow. Your student will pretend that these are gold nuggets. You can also use colorful pebbles, such as those used in fish tanks.

### Materials

For the Student

    marshmallows

    rock

    🖳 Let's Measure Mass Lab Sheet

    balance, primary

    cubes, centimeter/gram

    household items - assorted sizes (5)

    🖳 What's Your Gold Worth

    crayons, 16 or more

    markers, colored, 8 or more

    rocks - gold painted (5)

Optional

    checkers (20)

### Keywords and Pronunciation

**balance** : An instrument scientists use to find the mass of an object. To find an object's mass, place the object in one pan of a balance and add gram cubes to the other until the pans line up.

**gram** : A metric unit of mass. Scientists often weigh objects using grams as the measuring unit.

**kilogram** : The base metric unit of mass. A thousand grams make up one kilogram.

**mass** : The amount of matter in an object. Scientists use a balance to measure mass.

# LEARN
## Activity 1: Marshmallow Mass (Online)
### Safety
This lesson involves eating or using food. Before beginning, check with your doctor, if necessary, to assess whether your student will have any allergic reaction to this food.

## Activity 2: Mass (Online)

## Activity 3: Measure that Mass (Online)

## Activity 4: What's Your Gold Worth? (Online)

## Activity 5. Optional: Measuring Mass Review (Online)

---

# ASSESS
## Lesson Assessment: Let's Measure Mass (Online)
Your learning coach will help you complete an offline assessment covering the main objectives of this lesson. Your learning coach will score this assessment.

---

# LEARN
## Activity 6. Optional: Known Masses (Online)

Name _____                    Date _____

# What's Your Gold Worth?

Find the mass of each nugget and record it in the table below.

| Nugget # | | | | | |
|---|---|---|---|---|---|
| Mass | | | | | |
| Dollar Value | | | | | |

Use the data from the table above to make a bar graph of the masses of the gold nuggets.

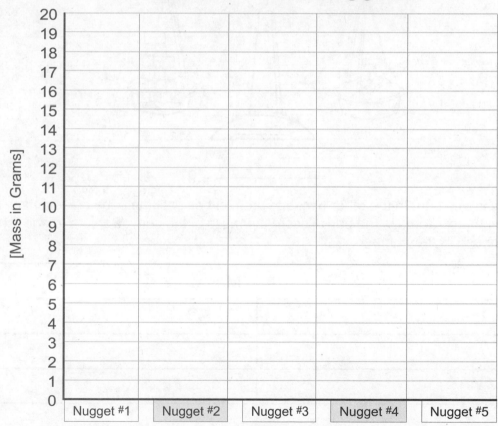

## Mass of Gold Nuggets

**Name** _____    **Date** _____

# Let's Measure Mass Lab Sheet

Look at the leveled balances.  Count the number of grams in the pans to determine the mass of each item.

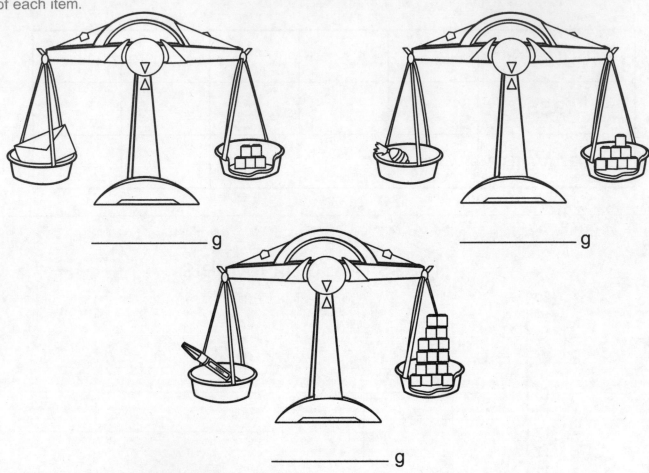

_____ g

_____ g

_____ g

Place an item in one pan. In the other pan, add gram cubes until the pans are level again. Count the number of grams in the pan. Record the mass of the item.  Be sure to add the units (g) at the end of the number.

| Item Name | Mass |
|-----------|------|
|           |      |
|           |      |
|           |      |
|           |      |
|           |      |

# Lesson Assessment

## *Let's Measure Mass*

**1.** What does a balance measure?

**2.** What did you measure when you weighed the gram cubes using the balance?

**3.** How many grams are in a kilogram?

**Refer to the What's Your Gold Worth activity sheet for the next two questions.**

**4.** What was the mass of your biggest nugget?

**5.** Chart the masses of your gold nuggets in a  bar graph.

# Student Guide
## Lesson 7: Spring into Action

### Lesson Objectives

- Demonstrate mastery of important knowledge and skills taught in this unit.
- Measure weight using a spring scale.
- Know that a newton is a metric unit of weight.
- Compare mass and weight.
- Identify some common tools used by scientists for measuring, such as a balance, a graduated cylinder, a metric ruler, and a thermometer.
- Identify four common metric units of measurement: centimeters, grams, milliliters, and degrees Celsius.
- Know that 100 centimeters equal 1 meter.
- Know that 1000 millimeters equal 1 meter.
- Measure temperatures on the Celsius scale.
- Identify the boiling point of water, the freezing point of water, and the average body temperature.
- Recognize that there are 1000mL in a liter.
- Measure volume in milliliters using a graduated cylinder.
- Record results on a bar graph.

# PREPARE

Approximate lesson time is 60 minutes.

## Materials

For the Student

- 📖 Let's Spring into Action
- 📖 Acting Like a Scientist Cutout Sheet

## Keywords and Pronunciation

**gravity** : The force that pulls all objects toward the Earth. The Earth's gravity keeps us from floating off into space.

**newton** : The metric unit of weight. This pair of scissors weighs .5 newtons.

**spring scale** : An instrument that measures weight. You can use a spring scale to weigh fruit at the grocery store.

**weight** : The pull of gravity on an object. Different objects of different sizes may sometimes have the same weight.

# LEARN
## Activity 1: Weighing In *(Online)*

## Activity 2: Gravity *(Online)*

## Activity 3: Spring into Action *(Online)*

## Activity 4: Acting Like a Scientist *(Online)*

---

# ASSESS

## Unit Assessment: Metrics and Measurements (*Online*)

Complete an offline Unit Assessment. Your learning coach will score this part of the Assessment.

---

# LEARN
## Activity 5. Optional: Going Shopping *(Online)*

# Acting Like a Scientist Cutout Sheet

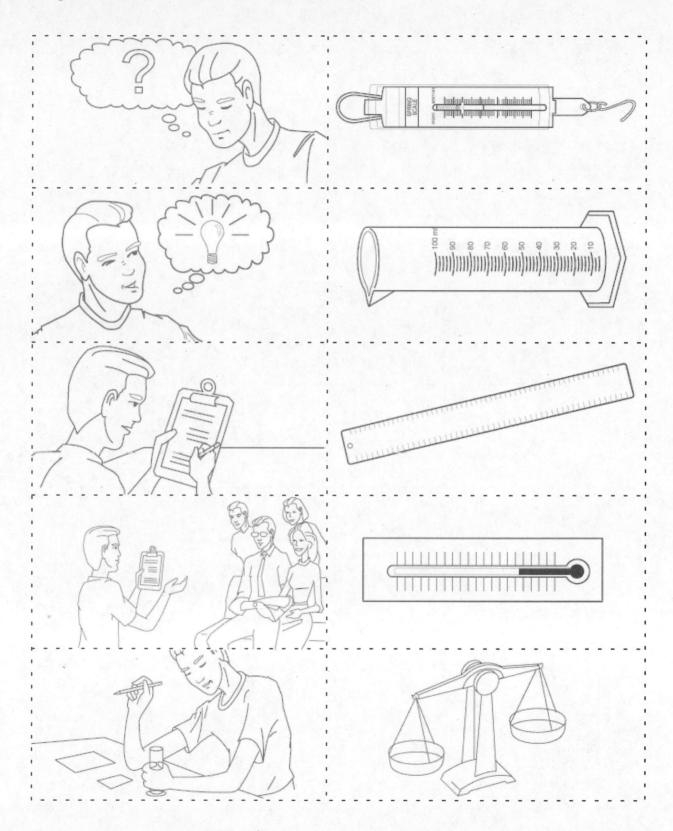

# Acting Like a Scientist Clues

Find the tool used to measure length. What units do you use to measure length?

(ruler, centimeters and meters)

Find the tool used to measure mass. What units do you use to measure mass?

(balance, grams)

Find the tool used to measure the volume of liquids. What units do you use to measure volume?

(graduated cylinder, milliliters and liters)

Find the tool used to measure temperature. What unit is used to measure temperature?

(thermometer, degrees Celsius)

Find the tool used to measure the weight of an object. What unit is used to measure weight?

(spring scale, newtons)

The scientific method starts with this step.

(question)

In this step, you make a smart guess about your question based on what you already know.

(hypothesis)

These are what we call the steps of an experiment.

(procedure)

This is information you collect and write down during an experiment.

(data)

In this step, you find out what your data means. It tells you what happened in your experiment.

(conclusion)

Name _____                Date _____

## Let's Spring into Action Lab Sheet

Write the names of the items you are going to measure in the first column in the table below. Weigh each of the items using the spring scale. Record your answers in the second column. Be sure to include the units as newtons. (N)

| Item | Weight |
|------|--------|
|      | _____ N |
|      | _____ N |
|      | _____ N |
|      | _____ N |
|      | _____ N |

Name _____ Date _____

# Unit Assessment

## *Spring into Action*

1. What unit of metric measurement do we use when we measure the temperature of something--millimeters or degrees?



2. What temperature does this thermometer show?

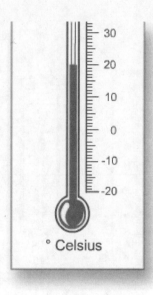

**3.** Which thermometer shows the temperature in Celsius at which water freezes?

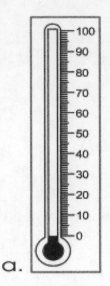 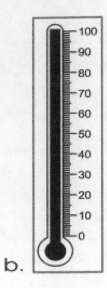

**4.** Which scientific tool would you use to measure how much milk is in a glass?

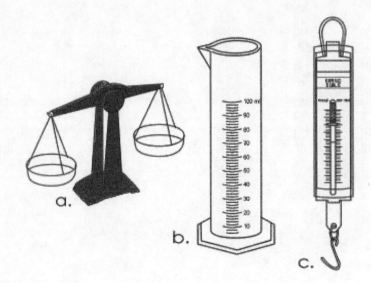

**5.** If you measured the volume of liquid in a graduated cylinder, would you use milliliters or centimeters?

**6.** Which is a greater volume--1 milliliter or 1 liter?

**7.** If you measured the length of a book, what metric units would you use--centimeters or milliliters?

**8.** Which scientific tool is used to measure mass?

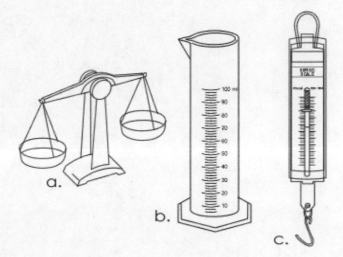

a.

b.

c.

**9.** What could a scientist use to show information that has been collected--a bar graph or a thermometer?

# Student Guide
## Lesson 1: Make It Move with Pushes and Pulls

- Demonstrate that a force is a push or a pull that can make an object move, that an object changes position when moved, and that the size of the change is related to the strength, or the amount of force, of the push or pull.
- Determine that moving heavy objects requires more force than moving light objects.
- Observe how the force of friction affects the movement of objects; know that friction works in the direction opposite the motion to slow down or stop sliding objects; and know that friction occurs whenever two types of matter move against each other.
- Identify gravity as the force that causes all things to fall toward the Earth.
- Observe that gravity makes objects fall at the same rate.

## Lesson Objectives

- State that a force is a push or a pull that can make something move.
- Compare how objects move, both in and out of water.
- Describe the changes in an object's position, due to motion.

# PREPARE

Approximate lesson time is 60 minutes.

## Advance Preparation

- You will need an assortment of small objects, such as a toy ball, styrofoam balls, paper clip, pen, rock, leaf, fork, spoon, stuffed animals, and action figures for this lesson. Your student will use these objects to observe how push and pull forces work.

## Materials

For the Student

    leaf

    pen, ballpoint

    pencils, no. 2

    rock

    fork

    paper clips

    spoon

    table

    toys - small; ball, etc.

    pan, baking - 9" x 13"

    styrofoam balls - small

    paper, 8 1/2" x 11"

    water

Optional

   🖳 Pushes and Pulls Review

    crayons, 16 or more

**Keywords and Pronunciation**

**force** : A push or a pull that can make an object move. The force of the wind pushed the door open.

**pull** : To tug on an object. The children liked to pull on the rope to ring the bell.

**push** : To press against an object. The mother pushed the baby carriage up the hill.

---

# LEARN
## Activity 1: Push and Pull (Online)

## Activity 2: Teeli the Dolphin (Online)

## Activity 3: Make It Move! (Online)

## Activity 4: Make It Move on Water (Online)

## Activity 5. Optional: Pushes and Pulls (Online)

---

# ASSESS

## Lesson Assessment: Make It Move with Pushes and Pulls (Online)

Your learning coach will help you complete an offline assessment covering the main objectives of this lesson. Your learning coach will score this assessment.

---

# LEARN
## Activity 6. Optional: Push and Pull Hunt (Online)

---

Name _____    Date _____

# Push and Pull Activity Sheet

Color in red the pictures that show the push force. Color in blue the pictures that show the pull force.

# Lesson Assessment

## *Make It Move with Pushes and Pulls*

1. What is force?

2. How can you make a pencil move?

3. What happens to an object when you move it?

4. What can you do to make an object in water change position that you cannot do when the object is out of the water?

5. In which direction will an object move if you pull it?

6. In which direction will an object move if you push it?

# Student Guide
## Lesson 2: Measuring Pushes and Pulls

### Lesson Objectives
- Measure the weight of objects using a spring scale.
- Know that moving heavy objects requires more force than moving light objects.
- Measure the forces needed to pull objects across a smooth, flat surface using a spring scale.

---

# PREPARE

Approximate lesson time is 60 minutes.

### Materials
For the Student
- book
- pencils, no. 2
- shoeboxes - of identical size (2)
- Measuring Pushes and Pulls
- rolling pin
- ruler, standard 12"
- scale, spring
- wood block
- blocks
- Elmer's Glue-All
- flashlight
- fork
- shoe
- string

Optional
- tape, masking

### Keywords and Pronunciation
**force** : A push or a pull that makes an object move. He used force to push the couch out of the way.

**weight** : The pull of gravity on an object. The weight of the brick was greater than the weight of the ball.

---

# LEARN
## Activity 1: Push And Pull Review *(Online)*

**Activity 2: Up on a Sled, Part 1** *(Online)*

**Activity 3: Heavy and Light** *(Online)*

**Activity 4: Up on a Sled, Part 2** *(Online)*

**Activity 5: Measuring Pushes and Pulls** *(Online)*

**Activity 6. Optional: Snow on Saturday** *(Online)*

___

## ASSESS

### Lesson Assessment: Measuring Pushes and Pulls (*Online*)

Your learning coach will help you complete an offline assessment covering the main objectives of this lesson. Your learning coach will score this assessment.

___

## LEARN
### Activity 7. Optional: Weighing In *(Online)*

Name _____     Date _____

# Measuring Pushes and Pulls

Tie the object to the spring scale. Pull the object slowly across the table. Record (in newtons) the amount of force needed to move the object. Measure and record (in newtons) how much each object weighs.

| Object | Force Needed to Pull Object | Weight of Object |
|---|---|---|
| | | |
| | | |
| | | |
| | | |
| | | |
| | | |
| | | |
| | | |

# Lesson Assessment

## *Measuring Pushes and Pulls*

1. Does it take more force to move a brick or a pencil?

2. Look at your Measuring Pushes and Pulls activity sheet. Which object took the most force to move?

3. Look at your Measuring Pushes and Pulls activity sheet. Did the item that took the most force to move also weigh the most?

4. Look at your Measuring Pushes and Pulls activity sheet. Was the item that took the least force to move also the one that weighed the least?

# Student Guide
## Lesson 3: We've Got Friction

## Lesson Objectives

- Know that friction is a force that slows down or stops sliding objects.
- Know that there is a force of friction whenever two surfaces move against one another.
- Demonstrate how the force of friction affects the motion of objects.

# PREPARE

Approximate lesson time is 60 minutes.

## Advance Preparation

- For this Science lesson, find five different surfaces that would exert different amounts of friction on a sliding shoe. A tile floor, a carpet, a cement patio, and a wooden deck would work well. Use the spring scale to test your student's shoe on a variety of surfaces to make sure the forces are within the range of the scale. You may need to select a shoe with soles that create more or less friction.

## Materials

 For the Student
  📠 Measuring Friction
   pencils, no. 2
   scale, spring
   shoe - child's, rubber-soled
  Optional
   string
   pan, baking - 9" x 13"
   tape, masking
   toys - car
   water - to fill pan
  📠 Friction Crossword Puzzle
   paper, 8 1/2" x 11"

## Keywords and Pronunciation

**friction** : The force that slows down and stops sliding objects. The friction between the sled runners and the snow helped slow down the sled.

# LEARN
## Activity 1: What Is Slowing Me Down? *(Online)*

## Activity 2: Understanding Friction *(Online)*

## Activity 3: Our Soles Keep Us Grounded *(Online)*

## Activity 4: Air Friction and Water Friction *(Online)*

## Activity 5. Optional: Reviewing Friction *(Online)*

---

# ASSESS

## Lesson Assessment: We've Got Friction (*Online*)

Your learning coach will help you complete an offline assessment covering the main objectives of this lesson. Your learning coach will score this assessment.

---

# LEARN
## Activity 6. Optional: Toy Cars and Friction *(Online)*

Name _____    Date _____

# Measuring Friction

Predict which surfaces will cause the most friction on your shoe. Then, list them in order, from greatest to least:

_____ **Greatest friction**

_____

_____

_____ **Least friction**

Pull your shoe across each surface using the spring scale, and measure (in newtons) how much force is needed to overcome the friction. Record your results below.

## Surface                                         Force (newtons)

_____    _____N

_____    _____

_____    _____

_____    _____

_____    _____

_____

# Was your prediction proven true or false?

Circle one.   **True        False**

Name                                          Date

# Friction Crossword Puzzle

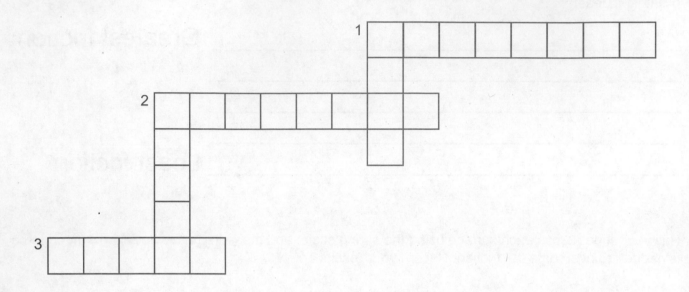

**ACROSS:**

1. There is a force of friction whenever two _____ move against each other.

2. This force slows down or stops sliding objects.

3. In your experiment with the toy car, which surface caused more friction: water or air?

**DOWN:**

1. The friction caused by a baseball player sliding into home will cause him to _____ down and eventually stop.

2. Friction is a _____ that slows down or stops sliding objects.

**Word Bank**

| force | water | slow | friction | surfaces |

# Lesson Assessment

## *We've Got Friction*

**1.** What force is created when two surfaces move against each other?

**2.** How did you test that the force of friction affects the amount of force needed to pull your shoe?

**3.** What effect does the force of friction have on a sliding object?

# Student Guide
## Lesson 4: Groovy Gravity

Gravity is a force that causes all things to fall to Earth. Your student will perform experiments to observe the force of gravity. Your student will experiment further by dropping items of various sizes and weights, to see whether gravity makes all objects fall at the same rate. He will look at pictures of people walking on the moon and learn that gravity on the moon is weaker than gravity on Earth.

### Lesson Objectives
- State that gravity pulls objects straight down to the Earth.
- Demonstrate how gravity affects all objects.
- Know that gravity makes all objects fall at the same rate.

---

# PREPARE

Approximate lesson time is 60 minutes.

### Materials
    For the Student
        meter stick, 100 cm
        pencils, no. 2
        string - about 35 cm
        📖 Gravity Makes Things Fall
        crayons, 16 or more
        dime
        marbles - one large, one small (2)
        quarter
        blocks - wood, square
        buttons - one large, one small (2)
        cookie sheet
        cubes, centimeter/gram
    Optional
        📖 Gravity Under the Big Top
        paper, 8 1/2" x 11" (4)

### Keywords and Pronunciation
**gravity** : The force that pulls objects down to the Earth. When you jump into the air, the force of gravity pulls you back down.

# LEARN
## Activity 1: What Is Force? *(Online)*

## Activity 2: Gravity At Work *(Online)*

## Activity 3: Going Down *(Online)*

## Activity 4: Gravity Makes Things Fall *(Online)*

## Activity 5. Optional: Groovy Gravity Review *(Online)*

---

# ASSESS

## Lesson Assessment: Groovy Gravity (*Online*)

Your learning coach will help you complete an offline assessment covering the main objectives of this lesson. Your learning coach will score this assessment.

---

# LEARN
## Activity 6. Optional: Gravity and Airplanes *(Online)*

---

Name _____    Date _____

# Gravity Makes Things Fall

On the chart, circle the item in each pair that you predict will fall faster. Circle both if you think they will fall at the same rate. Hold the two objects at shoulder height and drop them at the same time. Record which item hits the cookie sheet first.

| Hypothesis | Results |
| --- | --- |
| large marble  \|  small marble | |
| dime  \|  quarter | |
| wood block  \|  gram cube | |
| crayon  \|  pencil | |
| small button  \|  large button | |

Were your predictions correct about which objects would fall faster?

_____

Which pair of objects did not fall at the same rate?

_____

Why did this happen?

_____

Name _____

Date _____

## Gravity Under the Big Top

At the circus, you can see people try to work against gravity. Write the word "Gravity" anywhere you see gravity pulling objects or people down to Earth.

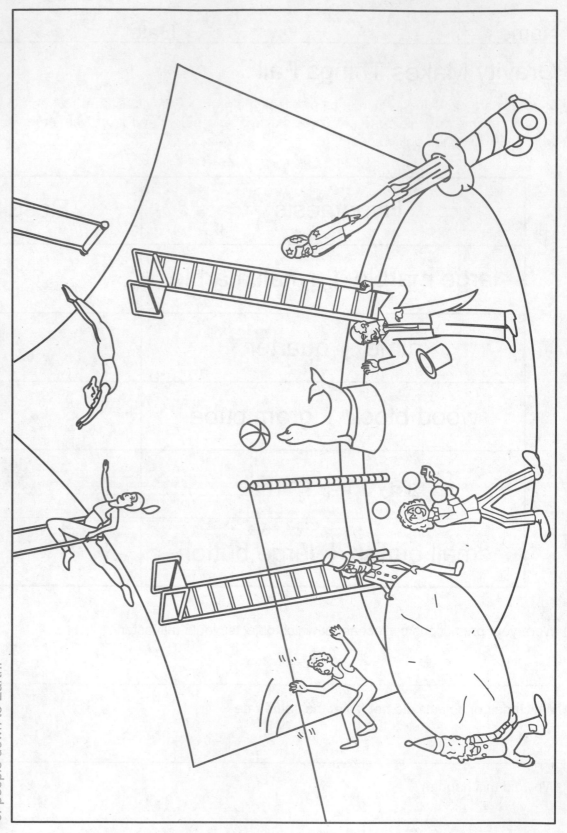

Name _____ Date _____

# Lesson Assessment

## *Groovy Gravity*

**1.** If you toss a ball up in the air it will fall straight back down to Earth because of what invisible force?

**2.** Using a ball, describe how gravity affects objects.

**3.** What happens if you drop two balls of different weights at the same time?

# Student Guide
## Lesson 5. Optional: Biography: Isaac Newton

### Lesson Objectives
- Know that Isaac Newton developed new ideas about friction and gravity.
- Know that as the force of gravity makes an object fall to the ground, the force of friction acts in the direction opposite to the motion.

---

# PREPARE

Approximate lesson time is 60 minutes.

### Materials

For the Student

 pencils, no. 2

 paper, 8 1/2" x 11"

Optional

 crayons, 16 or more

 sand - dry, 2 cups

 can, tin - coffee can with lid

 thermometer

---

# LEARN
## Activity 1. Optional: Optional Lesson Instructions *(Online)*

This lesson is OPTIONAL. It is provided for students who seek enrichment or extra practice. You may skip this lesson.

If you choose to skip this lesson, then go to the Plan or Lesson Lists page and mark this lesson "Skipped" in order to proceed to the next lesson in the course.

## Activity 2. Optional: Isaac Newton and the Invisible Force *(Online)*

## Activity 3. Optional: Another Great Discovery *(Online)*

## Activity 4. Optional: Newton Review *(Online)*

## Activity 5. Optional: Heating Up *(Online)*

---

# Student Guide
## Lesson 6. Optional: Gravity and Friction

### Lesson Objectives

- Demonstrate how the force of friction works on an object in the direction opposite to its motion.
- Know that objects of all shapes experience friction when falling.
- Determine which shapes are most affected by friction.

# PREPARE

Approximate lesson time is 60 minutes.

### Materials

For the Student

    📖 Friction Puts Up a Fight

    3-hole punch

    pencils, no. 2

    plastic sandwich bags, zipper-closed (3)

    quarters (4)

    string - 25cm each (12)

    tape, clear

    foil, aluminum - 10 cm squares (2)

    pan, baking - 9" x 13"

    water

### Keywords and Pronunciation

**friction** : The force that slows down and stops sliding objects. The friction between the sled runners and the snow helped slow down the sled.

**gravity** : The force that pulls objects down to the Earth. When you jump into the air, the force of gravity pulls you back down.

# LEARN

## Activity 1. Optional: Optional Lesson Instructions *(Online)*

This lesson is OPTIONAL. It is provided for students who seek enrichment or extra practice. You may skip this lesson.

If you choose to skip this lesson, then go to the Plan or Lesson Lists page and mark this lesson "Skipped" in order to proceed to the next lesson in the course.

## Activity 2. Optional: Friction Puts Up a Fight *(Online)*

## Activity 3. Optional: Friction and Gravity *(Online)*

## Activity 4. Optional: A Parachute for George Washington *(Online)*

## Activity 5. Optional: Emergency at Undersea *(Online)*

## Activity 6. Optional: Gravity Review *(Online)*

## Activity 7. Optional: More Experiments with Gravity and Friction *(Online)*

Name _____     Date _____

# Friction Puts Up a Fight Lab Sheet

Which parachute will fall the slowest and be the safest?

Predict which parachute will fall the fastest. In the prediction column, write a 1 next to the parachute that will fall fastest. Write a 2 next to the parachute that will fall at a medium speed, and a 3 next to the parachute that will fall the slowest.

|  | Hypothesis | Results |
|---|---|---|
| 10 cm parachute |  |  |
| 15 cm parachute |  |  |
| 20 cm parachute |  |  |

Carefully stand on a chair and drop the quarter with no parachute and the smallest parachute at the same time. Repeat with the other two parachutes. In the results column, write the order in which they fell. Write a 1 for the fastest, 2 for medium speed, and 3 for the slowest.

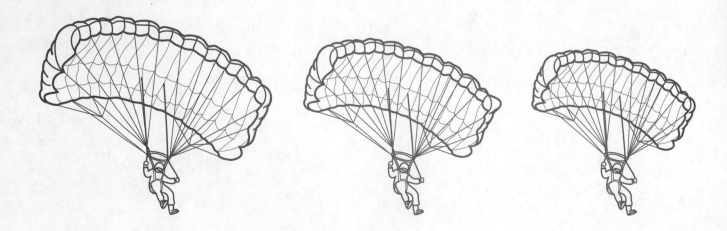

Circle the parachute that will fall the slowest and will be the safest.

# Student Guide
## Lesson 7: Balancing Act

## Lesson Objectives

- Demonstrate mastery of the knowledge and skills taught in this unit.
- State that a force is a push or a pull that can make something move.
- Measure the forces needed to pull objects across a smooth, flat surface using a spring scale.
- Know that friction is a force that slows down or stops sliding objects.
- Know that there is a force of friction whenever two surfaces move against one another.
- Demonstrate how gravity affects all objects.
- Know that gravity makes all objects fall at the same rate.

---

# PREPARE

Approximate lesson time is 60 minutes.

## Materials

For the Student

📖 Motion Bingo

pencils, no. 2

buttons (16)

Optional

card stock

fork

fruits - assorted, several

paper clips

spoon

toys - assorted, several

## Keywords and Pronunciation

**balance point** : Another name for center of gravity. Henry found the balance point of the long piece of wood.

**center of gravity** : A point around which the weight of an object is equally distributed. The waitress found the center of gravity of the large tray as she balanced it on one hand.

**gravity** : A force that pulls objects down to the Earth. When the apple fell off the tree, gravity pulled it to the ground.

---

# LEARN
## Activity 1: Forces And Motion Unit Review *(Online)*

---

# ASSESS
## Unit Assessment: Balancing Act (*Online*)
Your learning coach will help you complete an offline assessment covering the main objectives of this lesson. Your learning coach will score this assessment.

---

# LEARN
## Activity 2. Optional: Balance and Gravity *(Online)*
This activity is OPTIONAL. It is provided for students who seek enrichment or extra practice. You may skip this activity and proceed to the next activity in the lesson.

## Activity 3. Optional: Balancing Betsy, Part One *(Online)*
This activity is OPTIONAL. It is provided for students who seek enrichment or extra practice. You may skip this activity and proceed to the next activity in the lesson.

## Activity 4. Optional: Stay Up! *(Online)*
This activity is OPTIONAL. It is provided for students who seek enrichment or extra practice. You may skip this activity and proceed to the next activity in the lesson.

## Activity 5. Optional: Balancing Betsy, Part Two *(Online)*
This activity is OPTIONAL. It is provided for students who seek enrichment or extra practice. You may skip this activity and proceed to the next activity in the lesson.

## Activity 6. Optional: Finding Balance *(Online)*
This activity is OPTIONAL. It is provided for students who seek enrichment or extra practice. You may skip this activity and proceed to the next activity in the lesson.

Name _____          Date _____

## Motion Bingo Card

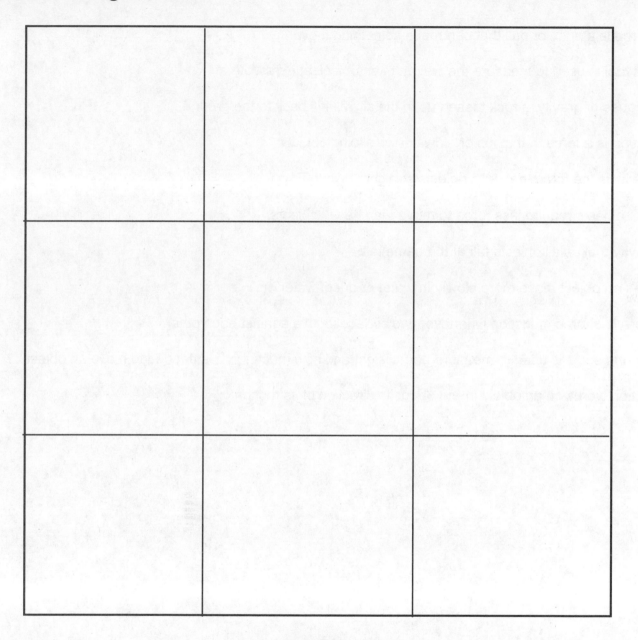

<table>
<tr><td></td><td></td><td></td></tr>
<tr><td></td><td></td><td></td></tr>
<tr><td></td><td></td><td></td></tr>
</table>

**Word Bank**

| | | | | |
|---|---|---|---|---|
| push | spring scale | force | surfaces | slows down |
| heavy | in water | rate | opposite | fall |
| pulls | | | | |

Name

Date

# Motion Bingo Clues

A force is a push or pull that can make something move.

This tool is used to measure the weight of an object. spring scale

Because of gravity, a rock tossed up in the air will fall back to the ground.

Friction is a force that stops or slows down sliding objects.

Gravity is the force that pulls objects straight down to Earth.

Light objects require less force to move than heavy objects.

Gravity makes all objects fall at the same rate.

Does an object move more slowly in water or out of water? in water

There is a force of friction whenever two surfaces move against each other.

A spring scale is used to measure both weight and how much force is needed to move an object.

Friction works on an object in the opposite direction of its motion.

# Unit Assessment

## *Balancing Act*

1. A push or a pull is an example of a _____.

2. Which instrument did you use to
   measure the force (in newtons)
   needed to move an object?

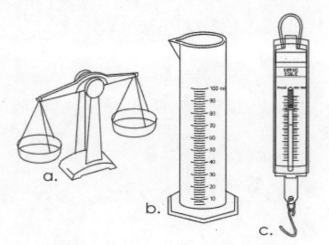

a.

b.

c.

3. Using any object that you can hold, demonstrate how gravity affects it.

4. If you dropped a large and a small ball at the same time from the same height, would
   one ball reach the ground first, or would both balls land at the same time?

5. If you slid a glass of milk across a table, what force would slow the glass down?

6. Yes or No: There is friction when any two objects rub against each other.

## *Student Guide*
## Lesson 1: What Are Machines?

- Demonstrate that it takes less force to pull a load up an inclined plane than it does to lift the load to the same height, but the load must travel a longer distance.
- State that wedges can be used to lift, cut, or separate objects.
- Explain how machines make work easier.
- Explain that wheels help reduce friction by allowing surfaces to roll instead of slide.
- Categorize common objects such as a lever, inclined plane, wedge, wheel and axle, pulley, and screw.
- Demonstrate how force is transferred between a wheel and an axle.
- Use moveable and fixed pulleys to lift loads.

### Lesson Objectives
- Explain how machines make work easier.
- Identify different types of simple levers.
- Define the scientific term *work*.
- Describe how levers can make lifting heavy loads easier.

# PREPARE

Approximate lesson time is 60 minutes.

### Advance Preparation
- For this Science lesson, unscrew the handle from a broom or mop. Measure the length of the handle and place pieces of masking tape around it to divide it into quarters.

### Materials
For the Student

    books

    broom - handle only

    rolling pin

    household items - bag with handles

    household items - tall plastic trashcan

    spoon - large, metal

    tape, masking

Optional

    hammer

    nail

    wood block

    What's a Machine?

    pencils, no. 2

    pencils, no. 2 - with flat edges

    penny (10)

    ruler, metric

## Keywords and Pronunciation

**force** : A push or a pull that can move an object. Gravity is a force that pulls objects toward the ground.

**fulcrum** (FUHL-kruhm) : The point on which a lever rests or turns. The base of a seesaw is its fulcrum.

**lever** : A bar for lifting or moving objects. A seesaw is an example of a lever.

**machine** : A device that makes work easier. A hammer is a simple machine.

**work** : To make an object move by applying a force. Work is needed to lift an object against the force of gravity.

---

# LEARN
## Activity 1: Going to Work *(Online)*

## Activity 2: Machines Make Work Easier *(Online)*

## Activity 3: Work, Force, and Motion *(Online)*

## Activity 4: Work With a Lever *(Online)*

## Activity 5. Optional: What's a Machine? *(Online)*

# ASSESS

## Lesson Assessment: What Are Machines? (*Online*)

Your learning coach will help you complete an offline assessment covering the main objectives of this lesson. Your learning coach will score this assessment.

---

# LEARN
## Activity 6. Optional: Simple Machine Trade-off *(Online)*

## Activity 7. Optional: Balancing Pennies *(Online)*

---

Name _____ Date _____

# What's a Machine?

Label the **lever** and the **fulcrum** on each of the levers.

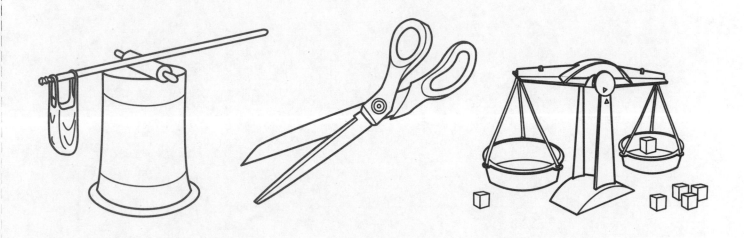

Point to and name the simple machine. Which person will use less force to pull out the nail?

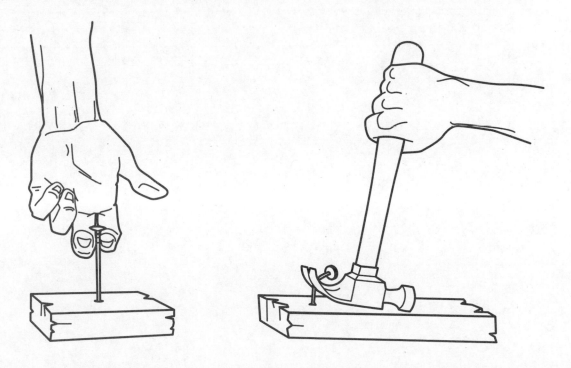

# Lesson Assessment

## *What Are Machines?*

1. What two things need to happen for work to be done?

2. What kind of simple machines are a seesaw and a balance?

3. Lifting a heavy bag with your hands can be difficult. How can you make the job easier?

4. What do people use to make work easier?

# Student Guide
## Lesson 2: Wheels and Axles

### Lesson Objectives

- Demonstrate how a force gets transferred between a wheel and its axle.
- Explain how wheels reduce friction by allowing surfaces to roll instead of slide.
- Identify wheels and axles.

# PREPARE

Approximate lesson time is 60 minutes.

### Advance Preparation

- For this Science lesson, cut two cardboard circles with a 6 cm diameter, and punch a hole in the center of each large enough for a pencil to fit through snugly. Gather a plastic strawberry basket for the activity.

### Materials

For the Student

    marbles (6)

    pencils, no. 2 - round (20)

    rock - small (6)

    scale, spring

    container, small plastic disposable

    paper clips - small

    string

    🖥 Wheels and Axles Lab Sheet

    1-hole punch

    cardboard, sheets - cut into circles

    pencils, no. 2 - unsharpened

    rubber bands (2)

    string - approximately 60 cm

    tape, masking

Optional

    vegetable oil

    can, tin - empty, grooves in top (2)

**Keywords and Pronunciation**

**axle** : A pole or rod attached to the center of a wheel. A bicycle wheel turns on an axle.

**rotate** : To turn around, or spin. The wheels on a car rotate as the car moves down the street.

**wheel** : Any circular object that spins around a center point. The wheels on a bicycle turn around.

---

# LEARN
## Activity 1: A New Machine *(Online)*

## Activity 2: What's a Wheel and Axle? *(Online)*

## Activity 3: Rolling Friction *(Online)*

## Activity 4: Use a Wheel and Axle *(Online)*

## Activity 5: Why Wheels and Axles are Useful *(Online)*

---

# ASSESS

## Lesson Assessment: Wheels and Axles (*Online*)

Your learning coach will help you complete an offline assessment covering the main objectives of this lesson. Your learning coach will score this assessment.

---

# LEARN
## Activity 6: Simple Ball Bearings Demonstration *(Online)*

## Activity 7: Ball Bearings With a Lubricant *(Online)*

---

Name _____          Date _____

# Wheels and Axles Lab Sheet

## Part 1

Label the wheel and axle.

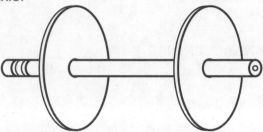

## Part 2

Make your predictions and record your observations.

**Question:**
Does lifting the container by turning the axle take more, less, or the same amount of work as lifting it by turning the wheels?

**Hypothesis:**
Lifting the container by turning the axle takes **MORE**, **LESS**, or **THE SAME AMOUNT OF** work as lifting it by turning the wheels. (Circle one)

**Procedure:**
1. Place a weight, such as a piece of fruit, into the container.
2. Stand next to a chair.
3. Turn the axle with your fingers to lift the container. Counting each natural turn of your fingers as one turn, determine the number of turns it takes to lift the container to the seat of the chair.
4. Unwind the string and lower the container to the floor.
5. Now turn the wheels with your hands to lift the container. Counting each natural turn of your hands as one turn, determine how many turns it takes to lift the container to the seat of the chair.

**Data:**
Did the load seem lighter when you lifted the container by turning the wheels or turning the axle?

_____

Name _____        Date _____

# Wheels and Axles Lab Sheet

# Part 3

Fill in the blanks with the words MORE or LESS (referring to force), GREATER or SHORTER (referring to distance), or THE SAME AMOUNT OF.

When you turned the wheels to lift the container, it took _____ force, but you had to turn the wheels through a _____ distance.

When you turned the axle to lift the container, it took _____ force, but you had to turn the axle through a _____ distance.

The wheel turns _____ times while lifting the load.

No matter whether you turn the wheel or the axle, it takes _____ turns to lift the container.

# Lesson Assessment

## *Wheels and Axles*

**1.** Which is a wheel and axle--a car tire, a see saw, or a shovel?

.

**2.** If you had to move something very heavy, would it be easier to roll it on wheels or slide it?

**3.** When you turned the wheel to lift an object, it took _____ force, but you had to turn the wheel through a _____ distance.

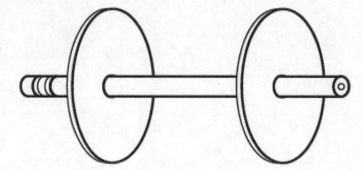

# *Student Guide*
## Lesson 3: Pulleys

### Lesson Objectives

- Identify how a fixed pulley is used to lift a load.
- Identify the parts of a pulley.
- Identify how a moveable pulley is used to lift a load.

---

# PREPARE

Approximate lesson time is 60 minutes.

### Advance Preparation

- For this Science lesson, view the steps in the investigation to become familiar with how to set up the fixed and moveable pulleys.

### Materials

For the Student

🖥 Pulleys

    meter stick, 100 cm

    pulley - additional

    scale, spring

    chair (2)

    household items - keys, less than 200

    string - heavy twine is preferable

    tape, masking

Optional

    pulley

🖥 Pulleys Crossword Puzzle

    string

### Keywords and Pronunciation

**pulley** : A grooved wheel that spins around a stationary axle. To lift an object, a person pulls on a rope resting in the groove of the wheel, and the wheel turns. The movers lifted the piano to the third floor with a pulley.

---

# LEARN
## Activity 1: Pulleys *(Online)*

**Activity 2: A Tree-Fort Pulley** (*Online*)

**Activity 3: Fixed and Moveable Pulleys** (*Online*)

**Activity 4. Optional: Pulley Puzzle Review** (*Online*)

---

# ASSESS

## Lesson Assessment: Pulleys (*Online*)

Your learning coach will help you complete an offline assessment covering the main objectives of this lesson. Your learning coach will score this assessment.

---

# LEARN

## Activity 5. Optional: Block and Tackle (*Online*)

Name_____ Date_____

# Pulleys

Label the grooved wheel and axle either "fixed pulley" or "moveable pulley". Draw an arrow to show which direction you pull on the string to lift the object. Draw another arrow to show the direction the object moves when you pull on the string.

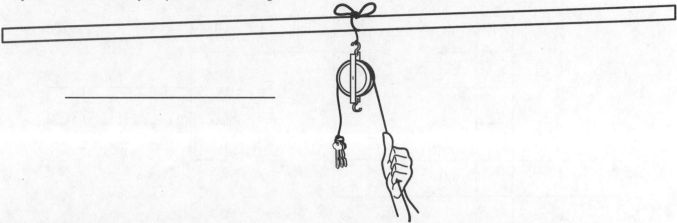

_____

Does the pulley move as an object is raised? _____

Weight of the keys_____N

Force needed to raise the keys_____N

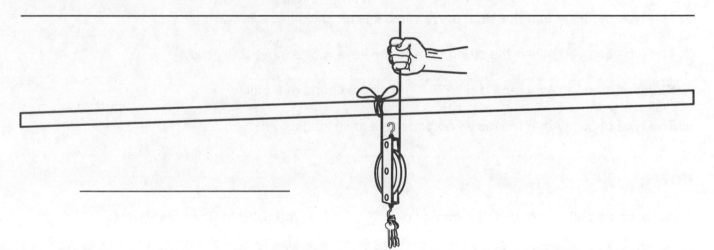

_____

Does the pulley move as an object is raised? _____

Weight of the keys_____N

Force needed to raise the keys_____N

Name _____                Date _____

# Pulleys Crossword Puzzle

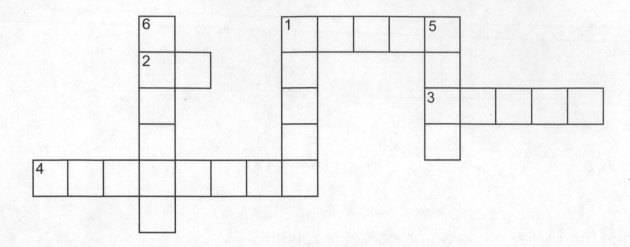

**ACROSS:**

1. The type of pulley that does not move when it is used to lift loads.

2. The direction you pulled the string to raise the keys with a moveable pulley.

3. String or rope, an axle, and a _____ are all parts of a pulley.

4. The type of pulley that moves when you use it to lift loads.

**DOWN:**

1. A moveable pulley reduces the amount of _____ you need to lift an object.

5. The direction you pulled the string to raise the keys with a fixed pulley.

6. A simple machine that has a grooved wheel attached to an axle that does not move.

**Word Bank**

| force | up | down | fixed | moveable | pulley | wheel |

# Lesson Assessment

## *Pulleys*

1. Which arrow is pointing to the grooved wheel on the pulley?

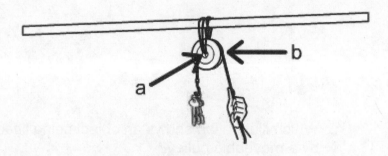

2. Which arrow is pointing to the axle on the pulley?

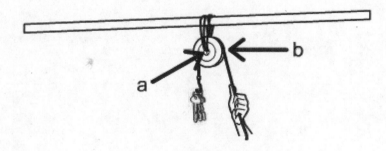

**3.** Which illustration shows an object being lifted by a fixed pulley?

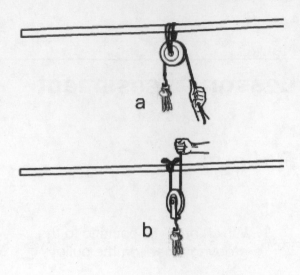

**4.** Which illustration shows an object being lifted by a moveable pulley?

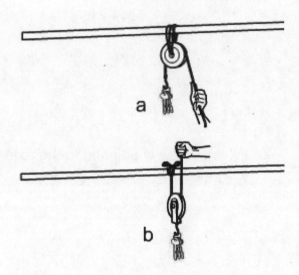

**5.** In which direction did you pull on the string when you lifted the keys with the moveable pulley--up or down?

**6.** Which type of pulley makes it easier to lift things by pulling down--a fixed or moveable pulley?

# Student Guide
## Lesson 4: Inclined Planes, Wedges, and Screws

### Lesson Objectives

- Explain that it takes less force to pull a load up an inclined plane than it does to lift the load to the same height.
- Explain that a load must travel a longer distance up an inclined plane than it would if it were lifted straight up to the same height.
- State that wedges can be used to lift, cut, or separate.
- Define a screw as a simple machine made of an inclined plane wrapped around a cylinder.

# PREPARE

Approximate lesson time is 60 minutes.

### Advance Preparation

- For this Science lesson, you will need to cut a right triangle out of cardboard. Make the base of the triangle 6 inches long.
- 
- For the Optional activity in this Science lesson, predrill two holes in a piece of wood.

### Materials

For the Student

    🖳 Inclined Planes Lab Sheet

    cardboard, sheets - smooth, 1 meter long

    meter stick, 100 cm

    pencils, no. 2 - 1 sharpened, 1 unsharpened (2)

    scale, spring

    string

    toys - car, less than 200 grams

    butter - 1-2 inch cube

    cardboard, sheets - triangle shaped

    knife, kitchen

    pencils, no. 2 - sharp and dull

    pencils, no. 2

    paper, 8 1/2" x 11"

    ruler, metric

    scissors, round-end safety

    tape, clear

    yarn

Optional
>  wood
>  ⬛ Planes, Wedges, and Screws
>  marker, black permanent, non-toxic
>  screw (2)
>  screwdriver

**Keywords and Pronunciation**

cylinder : A tube-shaped object with flat, circular ends. An orange-juice can is a cylinder.

---

# LEARN
## Activity 1: More Simple Machines *(Online)*

## Activity 2: Inclined Planes, Wedges, and Screws *(Online)*

## Activity 3: Inclined Planes *(Online)*

## Activity 4: Wedges *(Online)*

## Activity 5: Screws *(Online)*

## Activity 6. Optional: Planes, Wedges, and Screws Review *(Online)*

---

# ASSESS

## Lesson Assessment: Inclined Planes, Wedges, and Screws (*Online*)

Your learning coach will help you complete an offline assessment covering the main objectives of this lesson. Your learning coach will score this assessment.

---

# LEARN
## Activity 7. Optional: More on Screws *(Online)*

Name _____     Date _____

## Inclined Planes Lab Sheet

|  | Force (N) | Distance (cm) |
|---|---|---|
| Straight Up |  |  |
| Inclined Plane |  |  |

<u>Name</u>              <u>Date</u>

## Planes, Wedges, and Screws

Pretend you are out on a hike. You come to a steep hillside with two paths. One path goes straight up the steep hill. The other path winds back and forth up the top of the hill.

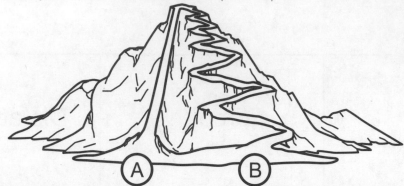

1. Which path would be easier to hike on to the top?
2. On which path would you walk the shortest distance?

Draw the missing wedges in each picture.

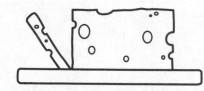

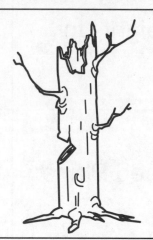

Challenge: Scissors are made of two kinds of simple machines. Circle both kinds.

 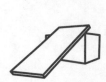  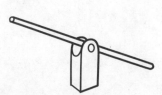

# Lesson Assessment

## *Inclined Planes, Wedges, and Screws*

1. Which mover is using more force to move the chair onto the moving van?

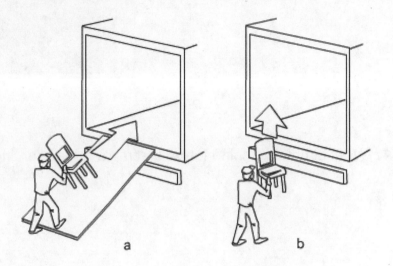

2. Which mover must move the chair a greater distance?

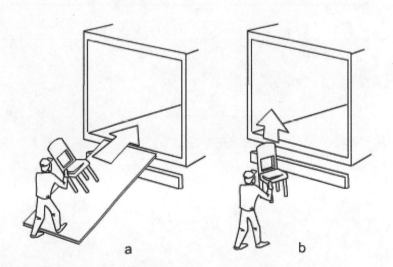

**3.** What simple machine is pictured here?

**4.** What simple machine forms a screw's thread--an inclined plane or a wedge?

# *Student Guide*
## Lesson 5: Machines Work Together

### Lesson Objectives

- Demonstrate mastery of important knowledge and skills taught in this unit.
- Identify common tools as simple or complex machines.
- Explain how machines make work easier.
- Identify different types of simple levers.
- Demonstrate how a force gets transferred between a wheel and its axle.
- Identify wheels and axles.
- Identify how a fixed pulley is used to lift a load.
- Identify the parts of a pulley.
- Identify how a moveable pulley is used to lift a load.
- Explain that it takes less force to pull a load up an inclined plane than it does to lift the load to the same height.
- State that wedges can be used to lift, cut, or separate.
- Define a screw as a simple machine made of an inclined plane wrapped around a cylinder.

# PREPARE

Approximate lesson time is 60 minutes.

### Advance Preparation

- For this Science lesson, gather as many common objects as you can to use as examples of simple and complex machines. The following objects work well, but you can substitute any number of readily available objects for those listed here:
- lever: broom
- wedge: doorstop, tacks, the cutter of a tape dispenser
- lever and wedge: hammer, scissors, nail, fork, kitchen knife, spoon, screwdriver, crowbar, shovel
- screw: wood screw
- wheel and axle: screwdriver, toy cars, tape dispenser

## Materials

For the Student

📖 What Kind of Machine is This?

    broom

    crow bar

    door knob

    doorstop

    hammer

    knife, kitchen

    nails

    nuts - with bolts

    pencils, no. 2

    play equipment - slide

    screw - wood

    screwdriver

    tacks

    fork

    household items - can opener

    household items - clothesline with pulley

    household items - door knob

    household items - window blinds with pulley

    paper, 8 1/2" x 11"

    scissors, adult

    shovel

    spoon

    tape, clear - dispenser

    toys - airplane or boat

    toys - car

Optional

    crayons, 16 or more

    paper, heavy

    markers, colored, 8 or more

# LEARN

## Activity 1: Simple Machines (Online)

### Safety

Some items used in this lesson may have sharp edges. Use caution when handling sharp objects, and do not let your student handle them.

**Activity 2: Brenda's Morning** *(Online)*

**Activity 3: Complex Machines** *(Online)*

**Activity 4: Simple Machines Unit Review** *(Online)*

---

# ASSESS
## Unit Assessment: Machines Work Together (*Online*)
Your learning coach will help you complete an offline assessment covering the main objectives of this lesson. Your learning coach will score this assessment

---

# LEARN
## Activity 5: Rube Goldberg's Crazy Contraptions *(Online)*

## Activity 6. Optional: Your Own Crazy Machine *(Online)*

---

Name _____          Date _____

# What Kind of Machine Is This?

Write the name of the machine in column 1. Write if the machine is simple or complex in column 2. Write the type or types of simple machines in column 3.

| Machine | Simple or Complex? | What Kind of Machine(s)? |
|---|---|---|
| Screwdriver | Complex | wedge, lever, wheel and axle |
|  |  |  |
|  |  |  |
|  |  |  |
|  |  |  |
|  |  |  |
|  |  |  |
|  |  |  |
|  |  |  |

# Unit Assessment

## *Machines Work Together*

1. Show how work can be done



2. Machines make work easier because they _____(increase or decrease) the amount of force needed to move an object.


3. Which illustration shows an object being lifted by a fixed pulley?

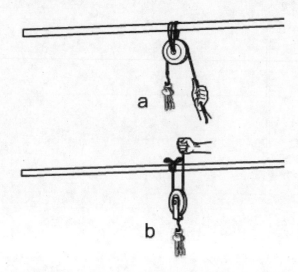

4. Which of the following uses a wheel and axle--a car, a seesaw, or a hammer?


5. When the wheel on a wheelchair turns, what else turns with it to make the chair move?

6. Which describes a pulley being used to make work easier--a) a person hammering a nail; b) a rope pulling an object using a grooved wheel; or c) someone sliding down a slide?

7. What simple machine is being used in the picture--a pulley or a wedge?

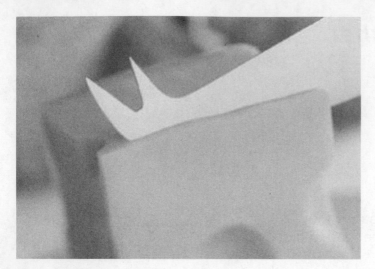

8. Which worker is using more force?

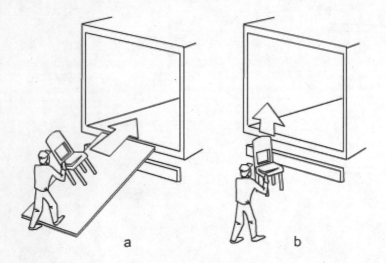

9. What type of simple machine is a long bar or pole that can lift or move heavy objects--a pulley or a lever?

10. What simple machine is the thread of a screw--an inclined plane or a lever?

11. Which illustration shows an object being lifted by a moveable pulley?

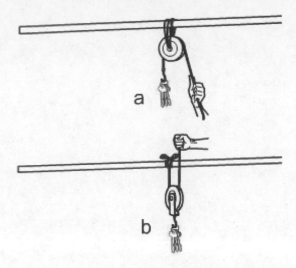

12. What simple machine is made of a wheel, an axle, and a rope?

13. Which type of pulley reduces the amount of force needed, or makes it easier to lift an object--a fixed or a moveable pulley?

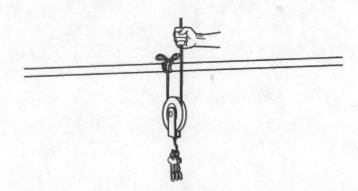

14. Which type of pulley makes it easier to lift an object up by applying force in the opposite direction--a fixed or a moveable pulley?

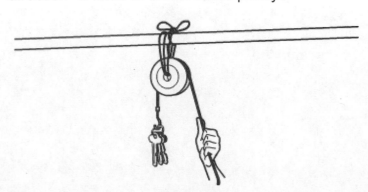

# Student Guide
## Lesson 1: The Force of Magnetism

- Observe that you can use magnets to make some objects move without touching them.
- State that magnets have two poles (north and south) and that similar poles repel each other and opposite poles attract each other.
- Observe that magnets are strongest at the poles, and compare relative strengths of magnets.
- Construct a temporary magnet and observe its magnetic properties.
- Recognize that the Earth is a large magnet, with magnetic poles and fields.
- Observe that the north-seeking pole of a bar magnet points to the north.

## Lesson Objectives

- Explain that magnets can cause some objects to move by exerting an invisible force.
- Identify magnets by their common names.
- Determine that objects made of iron and steel are attracted to magnets.
- Recognize that magnets are strongest at the poles.
- Determine the relative strengths of various magnets.

# PREPARE

Approximate lesson time is 60 minutes.

## Advance Preparation

- If you don't already have it, you will need the book *What Makes a Magnet?* by Franklyn Branley for the activities in this unit.

## Materials

For the Student

📖 Goin' Fishin' Lab Sheet

What Makes a Magnet? by Franklyn Branley ( ISBN 64451488 )

dimes

foil, aluminum

magnet, bar, pair

magnet, ring

magnet, u-shaped

magnets, bar, single

magnets, latch

nickel

pencils, no. 2

pins (2)

tacks (3)

twig

paper clips (3)

paper, 8 1/2" x 11"

penny

rubber bands (3)

string

chair

📖 Magnetic Strengths Lab Sheet

clothespin

table

tape, clear

Optional

paper, 8 1/2" x 11" - white

## Keywords and Pronunciation

**magnet** : an object that attracts certain metals, such as iron or steel; people often use magnets to attach notes to a refrigerator

**magnetic force** : The force between two magnets or between magnets and some metals. The magnetic force is what keeps a magnet attached to a refrigerator.

**magnetic pole** : The two ends of a magnet, where the magnetic force is especially strong. Bar magnets have two magnetic poles.

**magnetometer** (mag-nuh-TAH-muh-tur)

# LEARN
## Activity 1: Magnetic Forces (Online)

**Safety**

Never place magnets near a computer. When using magnets, do so at a safe distance from the computer.

## Activity 2: Magnetic Attraction *(Online)*

## Activity 3: Goin' Fishin' *(Online)*

## Activity 4: The Strongest Part of a Magnet *(Online)*

## Activity 5: Which Is Strongest? *(Online)*

## Activity 6. Optional: Magnetic Review *(Online)*

---

# ASSESS

## Lesson Assessment: The Force of Magnetism (*Online*)

Your learning coach will help you complete an offline assessment covering the main objectives of this lesson. Your learning coach will score this assessment.

---

# LEARN

## Activity 7. Optional: Magnet Race *(Online)*

---

Name _____          Date _____

# Magnetic Strengths Lab Sheet

Test the strength of three magnets.

|  | Magnet #1 | Magnet #2 | Magnet #3 |
|---|---|---|---|
| Type of magnet |  |  |  |
| Circle your prediction. | strongest<br>medium<br>weakest | strongest<br>medium<br>weakest | strongest<br>medium<br>weakest |
| How many clips did it pick up? |  |  |  |
| How many clips did it pick up this time? |  |  |  |

## Results:

The _____ magnet held the most paper clips.

## Conclusion:

The strongest was or were the _____. The weakest
was or were the _____.

Name _____     Date _____

# Goin' Fishin' Lab Sheet

List the objects you have gathered. Circle the names of the objects that you think will be magnetic. Place the objects in a box. Cast your line into the box. Write "Yes" or "No" to show if the object is magnetic and if it is made of iron or steel.

| Objects | Magnetic? | Iron or steel? |
|---------|-----------|----------------|
|         |           |                |
|         |           |                |
|         |           |                |
|         |           |                |
|         |           |                |
|         |           |                |
|         |           |                |
|         |           |                |
|         |           |                |
|         |           |                |

Conclusion _____

_____

_____

# Lesson Assessment

# *The Force of Magnetism*

1.  In your investigation, did you find that all magnets have the same amount of strength?

2.  Which will be attracted to a magnet--a nail or a cotton ball?

3.  Tell the name of each type of magnet.

4.  Use the magnet to pick up the paper clips without touching the clips.

5.  What part of the magnet picked up the most paper clips--the middle or the ends?

# Student Guide
## Lesson 2: Magnetic Poles and Fields

## Lesson Objectives

- State that magnets have poles—areas of greatest magnetic strength.
- Demonstrate that magnets have two kinds of poles, and that similar poles repel and opposite poles attract.
- Explain that the Earth is a large magnet with magnetic poles and a magnetic field.
- Show the magnetic fields of different magnets by using iron filings.

---

# PREPARE

Approximate lesson time is 60 minutes.

## Materials

For the Student

    pencils, no. 2

    🖳 What's the Attraction?

    magnet, bar, pair

    string

    tape, masking

    🖳 Magnetic Fields Lab Sheet

    iron filings

    magnet, bar, pair - assorted shapes

    magnet, ring

    magnet, u-shaped

    plates, paper

Optional

    glass, drinking

    household items - baby oil

    paper, 8 1/2" x 11"

    plastic wrap

    toys - marble magnets

## Keywords and Pronunciation

**attract** : To pull toward. Opposite poles of magnets attract each other.

**magnetic field** : The space around every magnet where the magnetic force can be felt. The Earth has a very large magnetic field.

**magnetic pole** : One of the two ends of a magnet, where the magnetic force is especially strong. Bar magnets have two magnetic poles, called north and south.

**repel** : To push away. Similar poles of magnets repel each other.

---

# LEARN
## Activity 1: The Ends of a Magnet *(Online)*
### Safety
Do not place magnets near a computer. When using magnets, do so at a safe distance from the computer.

## Activity 2: Fields and Poles *(Online)*

## Activity 3: Magnetic Poles *(Online)*

## Activity 4: Magnetic Fields *(Online)*
### Safety
Before handling iron filings, let the dust settle. Be mindful that your student does not ingest iron filings or get them in his eyes, or inhale the iron dust. Make sure he washes his hands after touching the filings.

## Activity 5. Optional: Magnetic Review *(Online)*

---

# ASSESS
## Lesson Assessment: Magnetic Poles and Fields (*Online*)
our learning coach will help you complete an offline assessment covering the main objectives of this lesson. Your learning coach will score this assessment.

---

# LEARN
## Activity 6. Optional: Odd Magnets *(Online)*

## Name _____         Date _____

# What's the Attraction?

Circle the word that describes how the magnets in each box would act.

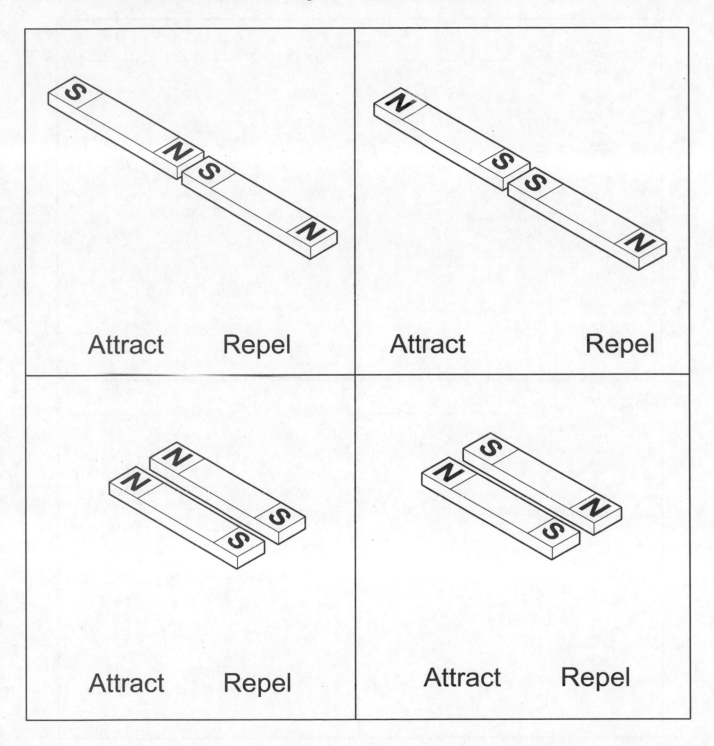

Attract          Repel          Attract          Repel

Attract          Repel          Attract          Repel

# Name_____     Date_____

## Magnetic Fields Lab Sheet

Draw each magnet and the position of the iron filings to show the magnetic field lines.

Shape of magnet:_____

Shape of magnet:_____

Shape of magnet:_____

Shape of magnet:_____

# Lesson Assessment

## *Magnetic Poles and Fields*

1. Place the two south poles of the magnets together. Do they repel or attract each other?

2. Place the north and south poles of the magnets together. Do they repel or attract each other?

3. Draw any type of magnet. Draw iron filings around it to show its magnetic field.

4. Where is a magnet's magnetic field strongest--in the middle or at the poles?

5. True or False: The Earth is like a big bar magnet because it has a north pole and a south pole.

# Student Guide
## Lesson 3: Temporary Magnets

### Lesson Objectives

- Explain how to make a temporary magnet.
- Explain that the molecules of an object made of iron or steel can be temporarily aligned to form a magnet.

---

# PREPARE

Approximate lesson time is 60 minutes.

## Materials

    For the Student

        What Makes a Magnet? by Franklyn Branley ( ISBN 64451488 )

        hammer

        magnet, bar, pair

        needle

        candle, votive

        matches

        paper clips (10)

    Optional

        magnets, bar, single

        nails - different sizes (3)

## Keywords and Pronunciation

**align** : To arrange in a straight line. After the orthodontist straightened my teeth, they were aligned.

**molecule** (MAH-lih-kyool) : Small particles that make up matter. A molecule is a small building block of matter.

**permanent** : Lasting for a very long time. The new dog became a permanent part of the family.

**temporary** : Lasting for a short time. When my relatives come to visit, I have to share my room with my cousin on a temporary basis.

---

# LEARN
## Activity 1: A Temporary Magnet *(Online)*
### Safety
Never bring magnets near a computer. When using magnets, do so at a safe distance from the computer.

---

## Activity 2: Magical Magnetism? *(Online)*

## Activity 3: Make a Temporary Magnet *(Online)*
**Safety**
Set up the votive candle where your student will not be able to burn himself on the flame. Keep the matches out of his reach.

## Activity 4. Optional: Magnet Review *(Online)*

---

# ASSESS
## Lesson Assessment: Temporary Magnets (*Online*)
Your learning coach will help you complete an offline assessment covering the main objectives of this lesson. Your learning coach will score this assessment.

---

# LEARN
## Activity 5. Optional: Magnetic Nails *(Online)*
**Safety**
Never use rusty nails. Be careful when handling sharp nails.

# Lesson Assessment

## *Temporary Magnets*

1.  How did you turn a regular needle into a magnet?

2.  Why is a magnetized needle called a temporary magnet--because it is magnetic for a little while or because it will pick up only paper clips?

3.  What happens when a temporary magnet loses its magnetism?

4.  The molecules of an object made of _____ can line up to make a temporary magnet.

# Student Guide
## Lesson 4. Optional: A Compass Is a Magnet

### Lesson Objectives

- Construct a simple compass.
- Identify the four cardinal directions.
- Recognize that a compass needle always points north.
- Recognize that the Earth has a geographic north pole and a magnetic north pole.
- Demonstrate the magnetic properties of magnetite.

# PREPARE

Approximate lesson time is 60 minutes.

## Advance Preparation

- Before you begin the lesson, locate the four cardinal directions in relation to your workspace.

## Materials

For the Student

What Makes a Magnet? by Franklyn Branley ( ISBN 64451488 )

cork - bottle (2)

magnet, bar, pair

marker, black permanent, non-toxic

needle

pencils, no. 2

rock samples - magnetite

bowl - Large, non-metallic

compass

paper clips

paper, 8 1/2" x 11"

water

Optional

🖳 Compass Review

crayons, 16 or more

cleaning items - steel wool

rock samples

bowl - large

## Keywords and Pronunciation

**compass** : An instrument that uses a magnet to navigate. The girl found her way back to camp by using her compass.

**magnetic north** : The north pole as indicated by a magnetic compass. Magnetic north is close to, but not exactly at, true north. When a compass needle points north, it points to the magnetic north of the Earth.

**needle** : The magnetized pointer of a compass. The needle of the compass swings around to point north.

**true north** : Earth's geographical north pole. On the top of a globe you can find true north.

---

# LEARN

## Activity 1. Optional: Optional Lesson Instructions *(Online)*

This lesson is OPTIONAL. It is provided for students who seek enrichment or extra practice. You may skip this lesson.

If you choose to skip this lesson, then go to the Plan or Lesson Lists page and mark this lesson "Skipped" in order to proceed to the next lesson in the course.

## Activity 2. Optional: Point the Way! *(Online)*

## Activity 3. Optional: Pointing North *(Online)*

## Activity 4. Optional: My Magnetic Compass *(Online)*

### Safety

Never place magnets near a computer. When using magnets, do so at a safe distance from the computer.

## Activity 5. Optional: Compass Review *(Online)*

## Activity 6. Optional: Mighty Magnetite *(Online)*

---

Name _____    Date _____

# Compass Review

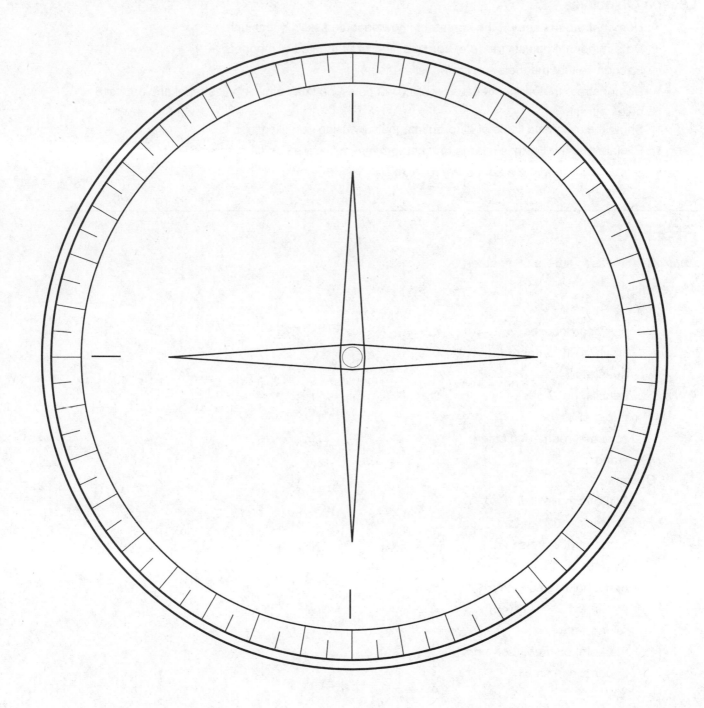

# Student Guide
## Lesson 5: Through Thick and Thin

### Lesson Objectives

- Demonstrate mastery of the important knowledge and skills of this unit.
- Determine that objects made of iron and steel are attracted to magnets.
- Recognize that magnets are strongest at the poles.
- Demonstrate that magnets have two kinds of poles, and that similar poles repel and opposite poles attract.
- Show the magnetic fields of different magnets by using iron filings.
- Explain that the Earth is a large magnet with magnetic poles and a magnetic field.
- Explain how to make a temporary magnet.

---

# PREPARE

Approximate lesson time is 60 minutes.

### Materials

For the Student

> cardboard, boxes
>
> crayons, 16 or more (2)
>
> needle
>
> pencils, no. 2
>
> paper clips (6)
>
> scissors, round-end safety
>
> string

Optional

> 🖳 Go Fish Review
>
> 🖳 Thick and Thin Lab Sheet
>
> cardboard, sheets (4)
>
> magnet, bar, pair
>
> household items - cloth
>
> paper, 8 1/2" x 11" (40)
>
> ruler, metric
>
> markers, colored, 8 or more
>
> paper clips - small

**Keywords and Pronunciation**

**magnetic field** : The space around every magnet where the magnetic force can be felt.

# LEARN
## Activity 1: Go Fish *(Online)*

Click Coming Attractions to review what you've learned about magnets. Then play a game of Go Fish.

# ASSESS
## Unit Assessment: Magnetism (*Online*)

Your learning coach will help you complete an offline assessment covering the main objectives of this lesson. Your learning coach will score this assessment.

# LEARN
## Activity 2. Optional: Magnetic Strength *(Online)*

This activity is OPTIONAL. It is provided for students who seek enrichment or extra practice. You may skip this activity and proceed to the next activity in the lesson.

### Safety

Never place magnets near a computer. When using magnets, do so at a safe distance from the computer.

## Activity 3. Optional: Magnetic Fields *(Online)*

This activity is OPTIONAL. It is provided for students who seek enrichment or extra practice. You may skip this activity and proceed to the next activity in the lesson.

## Activity 4. Optional: Thin and Thick *(Online)*

This activity is OPTIONAL. It is provided for students who seek enrichment or extra practice. You may skip this activity and proceed to the next activity in the lesson.

## Activity 5. Optional: Magnetic Maze *(Online)*

This activity is OPTIONAL. It is provided for students who seek enrichment or extra practice. You may skip this activity and proceed to the next activity in the lesson.

Name _____          Date _____

# Thick and Thin Lab Sheet

Follow the procedure and record your results.

| | 1 layer | | 1 cm thick | | 2 cm thick | |
| --- | --- | --- | --- | --- | --- | --- |
| | prediction | result | prediction | result | prediction | result |
| | | | | | | |
| | | | | | | |
| | | | | | | |

## PROCEDURE

Step 1:  Will the items block the magnet from attracting paper clips? Predict what will happen. Write what will happen. Write "yes" or "no" in the prediction columns for each item.

Step 2:  Test it.

Step 3:  Write "yes" or "no" in the results column depending on what happened to the paper clips when you wrapped each item around the glass.

Look at your data. Did the thickness of a material change the magnetic force going through it?      yes        no

How do you know? _____

Name　　　　　　　　　　　　　　　　Date

# Go Fish Review

Cut out each fish. Attach a paper clip to each fish's mouth.

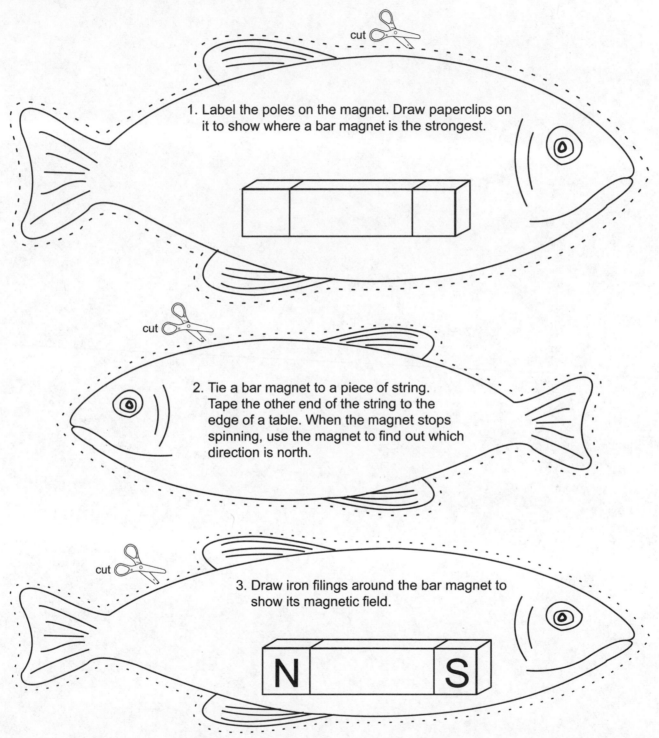

cut

1. Label the poles on the magnet. Draw paperclips on it to show where a bar magnet is the strongest.

cut

2. Tie a bar magnet to a piece of string. Tape the other end of the string to the edge of a table. When the magnet stops spinning, use the magnet to find out which direction is north.

cut

3. Draw iron filings around the bar magnet to show its magnetic field.

N　　　　　　S

# Go Fish Review

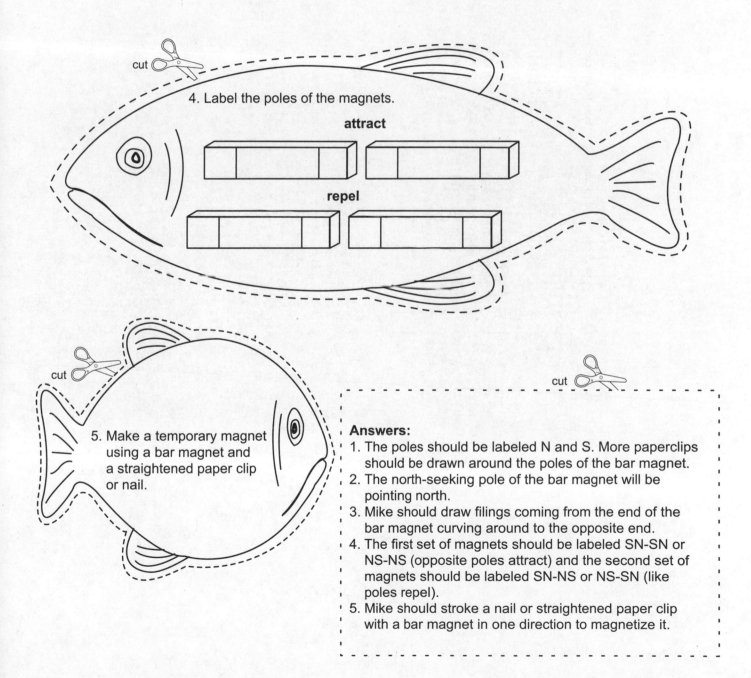

4. Label the poles of the magnets.

**attract**

**repel**

5. Make a temporary magnet using a bar magnet and a straightened paper clip or nail.

**Answers:**
1. The poles should be labeled N and S. More paperclips should be drawn around the poles of the bar magnet.
2. The north-seeking pole of the bar magnet will be pointing north.
3. Mike should draw filings coming from the end of the bar magnet curving around to the opposite end.
4. The first set of magnets should be labeled SN-SN or NS-NS (opposite poles attract) and the second set of magnets should be labeled SN-NS or NS-SN (like poles repel).
5. Mike should stroke a nail or straightened paper clip with a bar magnet in one direction to magnetize it.

# Unit Assessment

# *Magnetism*

1. Which would be attracted to a magnet--a paper clip or a plastic bag?

2. What part of a bar magnet is the strongest--the middle or the poles?

3. True or False: The north-seeking pole of a bar magnet points to the north because the Earth is a big magnet.

4. Which set of magnets will attract each other?

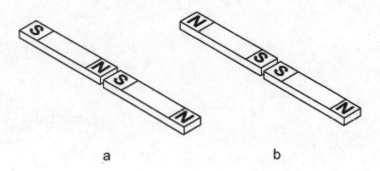

a                    b

5. What can you make by stroking a needle with a magnet many times in the same direction?

6. Iron filings sprinkled around a magnet line up with its magnetic _____.

# *Student Guide*
## Lesson 1: Sounds All Around

- Describe the sounds that a variety of objects make.
- Identify the sources of natural and man-made sounds.
- Explain how sound vibrations and sound waves travel.
- Differentiate between pitch and volume.
- Explain how pitch and volume change on a stringed instrument.
- Recognize that the sound of your voice is a result of your vocal cords vibrating.
- Tell about the life and accomplishments of Alexander Graham Bell.

## Lesson Objectives

- Determine the sources of a variety of sounds.
- Identify the source of natural and man-made sounds.

---

# PREPARE

Approximate lesson time is 60 minutes.

## Materials

For the Student

    💻 Super Sleuth

    pencils, no. 2

    paper, 8 1/2" x 11"

Optional

    clipboard

    💻 Noisy Ned's Bedroom

    crayons, 16 or more

    tape recorder - and cassette

## Keywords and Pronunciation

**sleuth** : A detective. A *sleuth* searches for information to solve a mystery.

---

# LEARN
## Activity 1: What Is Sound? *(Online)*

---

**Activity 2: Sounds Surround Us** *(Online)*

**Activity 3: Be a "Sound Sleuth"** *(Online)*

**Activity 4: Nature Walk** *(Online)*

**Activity 5. Optional: Noisy Ned's Bedroom** *(Online)*

---

# ASSESS

## Lesson Assessment: Sounds All Around (*Online*)

Your learning coach will help you complete an offline assessment covering the main objectives of this lesson. Your learning coach will score this assessment.

---

# LEARN

## Activity 6. Optional: Sound Effects *(Online)*

---

Name _____     Date _____

# Super Sleuth

*Sound #1 - Trainee Level*

What sounds do you hear?

_____

Where do you think these sounds are found?

_____


*Sound #2 - Detective Level*

What sounds do you hear?

_____

Where do you think these sounds are found?

_____


*Sound #3 - Super Sleuth Level*

What sounds do you hear?

_____

Where do you think these sounds are found?

_____

Name _____    Date _____

# Noisy Ned's Bedroom

When Ned comes home his bedroom will not be as quiet as it is now.  Color all the objects that make sounds.  Make boxes around the objects Ned can use to make sounds.  Circle the objects that make natural sounds.

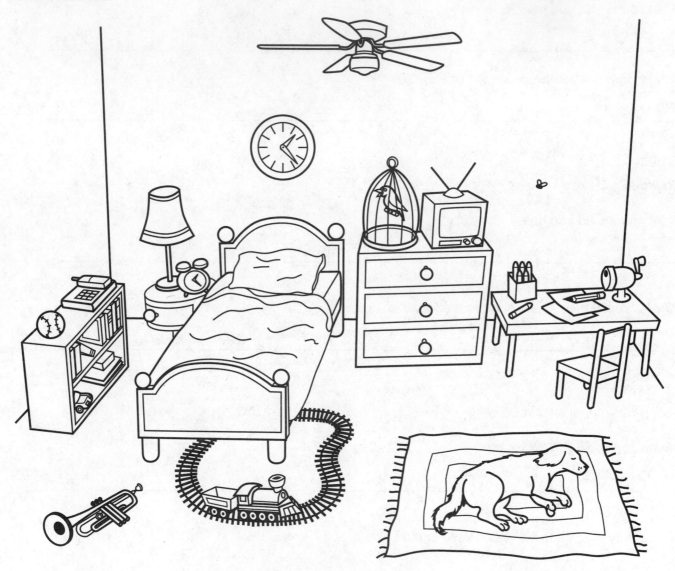

# Lesson Assessment

## *Sounds All Around*

1. Name three things in nature that make sounds.

2. Name three things you could do to make a sound.

3. Name a natural sound and a man-made sound you might hear on a walk outside.

4. Name three sounds that you might hear only when you are indoors, and tell whether they are natural or man-made sounds.

# Student Guide
## Lesson 2: Sound Waves

In this lesson, your student will listen to several sounds and determine what they are and how they were produced.

## Lesson Objectives

- Explain that sound is made by vibrating objects.
- identify vibrating sources of sound.

---

# PREPARE

Approximate lesson time is 60 minutes.

## Materials

For the Student
Optional
    rubber bands
    balloon - deflated
    pan, baking
    Slinky® - metal
    water
    tub - bathtub
    📖 Good Vibrations
    pencils, no. 2
    spoon
    string
    table
    tuning fork
    bowl
    rice
    tubs, margarine
    balloon
    household items - radio

## Keywords and Pronunciation

**wave** : A repetitive movement up and down or back and forth. You can spend all day watching ocean waves crash onto the shore.

---

# LEARN
## Activity 1: Sound Waves and Ocean Waves *(Online)*

## Activity 2: Sound Waves *(Online)*

## Activity 3: The Balloon *(Online)*

## Activity 4: Making Waves *(Online)*

## Activity 5: Name the Vibrating Object *(Online)*

## Activity 6. Optional: Reviewing Vibrations *(Online)*

---

# ASSESS

## Lesson Assessment: Sound Waves *(Online)*

Your learning coach will help you complete an offline assessment covering the main objectives of this lesson. Your learning coach will score this assessment

---

# LEARN

## Activity 7. Optional: Tuning-Fork Fun *(Online)*

### Safety

Teach your student how to strike a tuning fork on the heel of his hand. Never strike the tines of the fork on a hard object because this action can bend the tines.

## Activity 8. Optional: Dancing Rice *(Online)*

---

Name _____          Date _____

## Good Vibrations

| Listen, what's the sound? | What is vibrating? |
|---|---|
| 1. Slamming door | Door |
| 2. | |
| 3. | |
| 4. | |
| 5. | |
| 6. | |

# Lesson Assessment

## *Sound Waves*

1. Which would vibrate and produce a sound--a still rubber band or a plucked rubber band?

2. When an object is struck, what happens that produces a sound?

3. What vibrates when a door slams?

4. When you hear a stringed instrument like a harp, what vibrates to produce its sound?

# *Student Guide*
## Lesson 3: Sound Travels

### Lesson Objectives

- Demonstrate that sound waves travel through solids, liquids, and gases.
- Compare the loudness of sound passing through three different materials.

---

# PREPARE

Approximate lesson time is 60 minutes.

### Advance Preparation

- Remove the lid from a soup can. Clean the can thoroughly. Sand down the edges or tape masking tape all around the edges. Punch a hole in the center of the bottom of the can, using a nail and a hammer.

### Materials

    For the Student
        can opener
        hammer
        nail
        balloon
        can, tin
        rubber bands
        scissors, round-end safety
        tape, masking
        🖥 Sound Through Solids, Liquids, and Gases Lab Sheet
        plastic sandwich bags, zipper-closed
        straws, drinking
        wood block - same size as bags
        spoon
        water
    Optional
        fork
        string
        table
        toothpicks
        Elmer's Glue-All
        scissors, adult
        shoeboxes (2)

**Keywords and Pronunciation**

**amplify** : To make louder. When you turn up the volume on a radio, you amplify the sound.

**vibrate** : To move back and forth rapidly. Plucking a rubber band causes it to vibrate and make a sound.

# LEARN
## Activity 1: Sound Travels (Online)

## Activity 2: What Leena Heard (Online)

## Activity 3: The Sound Cannon (Online)

## Activity 4: Sounds Through Solids, Liquids, and Gases (Online)

## Activity 5. Optional: Reviewing Sound Travels (Online)

# ASSESS

## Lesson Assessment: Sound Travels (*Online*)

Your learning coach will help you complete an offline assessment covering the main objectives of this lesson. Your learning coach will score this assessment.

# LEARN
## Activity 6. Optional: Soundproof Chamber (Online)

Name _____          Date _____

# Sound Through Solids, Liquids, and Gases Lab Sheet

Question:  Which of these three types of material will amplify the sound the most, air, water, or wood?

Hypothesis:_____

Observations and Data: Listen to the sound. Write 1 for lowest volume, 2 for medium volume, and 3 for highest volume.

| Item | State of Matter | Volume |
|------|-----------------|--------|
| Air | | |
| Water | | |
| Wood | | |

Conclusion: Amplify means to make louder. Which material amplified the sound the most?

_____

In which bag did the sound seem the faintest?

_____

Name _____     Date _____

# Lesson Assessment

## *Sound Travels*

1. If you made a sound underwater, would someone else underwater be able to hear the sound you made?


2. Think back to the materials you tested today. When was the sound the loudest--when you tapped the bag of air, the bag of water, or the wood?


3. Listen when I call to you. What type of matter must the sound travel through to reach your ears?


4. Think back to the materials you tested today. When was the sound the softest--when you tapped the bag of air, the bag of water, or the wood?

# Student Guide
## Lesson 4: The Ears Hear

## Lesson Objectives

- Explain how sound is transmitted through the ear.
- Identify ways that animals use their ears to survive.
- Label the parts of the ear.

# PREPARE

Approximate lesson time is 60 minutes.

## Materials

For the Student

music or music tape

paper, colored construction, 12"x12"

toilet paper tubes

household items - radio or stereo

tape, masking

Optional

📖 How the Ears Hear

cotton balls

cardboard, sheets

paper towel tube (2)

## Keywords and Pronunciation

**anvil** : The second small bone in the middle ear, which moves in response to the hammer. The movements of the hammer make the anvil move.

**cochlea** (KOH-klee-uh) : The spiral-shaped part of the inner ear. The cochlea sends sound signals to the brain.

**eardrum** : A thin, skin-like division between the outer ear and middle ear that vibrates as sound waves pass through it to the three bones in the middle ear. The eardrum vibrates when sound waves strike it.

**hammer** : The first small bone in the middle ear, which moves as the eardrum vibrates. The hammer bone looks like a small hammer.

**outer ear canal** : The pathway that directs sound waves from the outer ear flap to the eardrum. Sound waves travel through the outer ear canal to the eardrum.

**outer ear flap** : The outer part of the ear that collects sound waves. The outer ear flap gathers sound waves and directs them into the ear.

**stirrup** : The third small bone in the middle ear, which moves in response to the anvil and passes sound waves to the inner ear. The stirrup is the smallest bone in the body.

# LEARN
## Activity 1: Different Ears for Different Jobs *(Online)*

## Activity 2: Catching Waves *(Online)*

## Activity 3: Journey into Your Ear *(Online)*

## Activity 4. Optional: How Your Ears Hear *(Online)*

---

# ASSESS
## Lesson Assessment: The Ears Hear (*Online*)

Your learning coach will help you complete an offline assessment covering the main objectives of this lesson. Your learning coach will score this assessment.

---

# LEARN
## Activity 5. Optional: How Well Do You Hear? *(Online)*

## Activity 6. Optional: Echo, Echo *(Online)*

Name

Date

# How the Ears Hear

Using the words provided, explain how we hear sound.

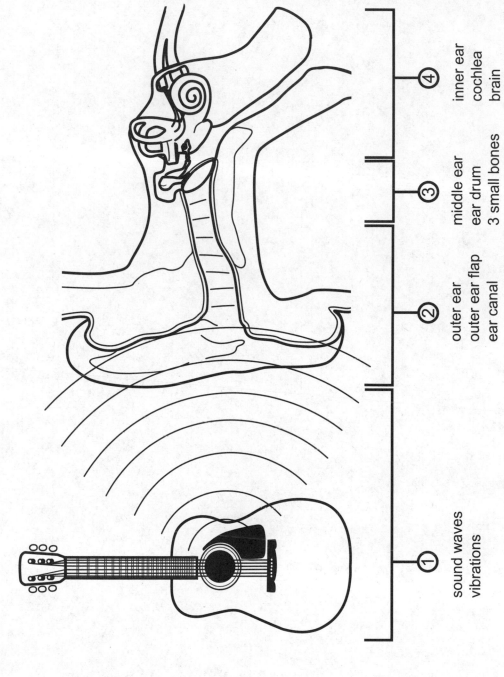

1   sound waves   vibrations

2   outer ear   outer ear flap   ear canal

3   middle ear   ear drum   3 small bones

4   inner ear   cochlea   brain

# Lesson Assessment

## *The Ears Hear*

1.  Point to the hammer, anvil, and stirrup bones.

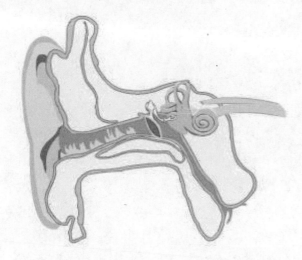

2.  True or False: An ear trumpet helps you hear better because its wider opening can collect more sound waves than your outer ear.

3.  Which vibrates first--the eardrum or the tiny bones in the middle ear?

4.  Find the part of the ear that has liquid and tiny nerve cells inside. What's the name of this part of the ear?

5.  Name two ways that an animal's ears can help the animal survive.

# *Student Guide*
## Lesson 5: Exploring Pitch and Volume

### Lesson Objectives

- Differentiate between pitch and volume.
- Experiment to see what causes pitch and volume changes.

---

## PREPARE

Approximate lesson time is 60 minutes.

### Materials

For the Student

    meter stick, 100 cm

    nails - different lengths (4)

    chair (2)

    household items - thread

    spoon - metal

    tape, masking

Optional

    toys - bicycle

    toys - playing cards

    pots - metal (3)

    ruler, standard 12"

    piping - plastic, 3 feet long

    saw

    saucepan - metal (2)

    bowl - plastic (2)

---

## LEARN
### Activity 1: Pitch and Volume *(Online)*

### Activity 2: Two Ways to Describe Sound *(Online)*

---

**Activity 3: Nail Chimes** *(Online)*

**Activity 4: Pitch and Volume Together** *(Online)*

**Activity 5: Pots and Pans** *(Online)*

**Activity 6. Optional: Review of Pitch and Volume** *(Online)*

---

# ASSESS

## Lesson Assessment: Exploring Pitch and Volume (*Online*)

Your learning coach will help you complete an offline assessment covering the main objectives of this lesson. Your learning coach will score this assessment.

---

# LEARN
## Activity 7. Optional: Make a Panpipe *(Online)*
**Safety**

Cut the pipes yourself, and do not let your student use the saw.

## Activity 8. Optional: Homemade Band *(Online)*

---

Name _____    Date _____

# Lesson Assessment

## *Exploring Pitch and Volume*

1. If we say a sound is loud or soft, are we describing its volume or pitch?


2. Which word could you use to describe pitch--loud or low?


3. Which would produce a high-pitched sound--a small bell or a large bell?


4. Describe a way you could increase the volume of a sound.

# *Student Guide*
## Lesson 6: Musical Sound

String instruments produce sound through vibrations caused by plucking or stroking the strings. The thickness, length, and tension of the strings determine pitch. In this lesson your student is introduced to stringed instruments. your student first discovers how sound is made by stringed instruments, integrating the concepts of pitch and volume; then he constructs his own example.

### Lesson Objectives

- Differentiate between methods of changing volume and pitch on a stringed instrument.
- Demonstrate how to change the pitch of a stringed instrument's sound.
- Demonstrate how to change the volume of a stringed instrument's sound.

# PREPARE

Approximate lesson time is 60 minutes.

### Advance Preparation

- For this Science lesson, make sure you have two rubber bands that are the same length, but one thick and one thin.

### Materials

    For the Student
        pencils, no. 2
        rubber bands - thick (2)
        rubber bands - thin (2)
        scissors, adult
        shoeboxes
    Optional
        rope - jump rope or thick

# LEARN
## Activity 1: What Can You Remember About Pitch and Volume? *(Online)*

## Activity 2: Elly's Surprise *(Online)*

## Activity 3: Explore Pitch and Volume (Online)

## Activity 4. Optional: Review of Stringed Instruments (Online)

---

# ASSESS

## Lesson Assessment: Musical Sound (Online)

Your learning coach will help you complete an offline assessment covering the main objectives of this lesson. Your learning coach will score this assessment.

---

# LEARN

## Activity 5. Optional: More Pitch and Volume at the Symphony (Online)

## Activity 6. Optional: Listen to Instruments (Online)

---

Name _____    Date _____

# Lesson Assessment

## *Musical Sound*

1. If you wanted to make a high-pitched sound using a stringed instrument, would you tighten the strings or pluck the strings harder?

2. If you wanted to make a soft sound with a stringed instrument, would you make the strings shorter or pluck the strings lightly?

3. Show how you can change the pitch of your stringed instrument.

4. Show how you can change the volume of your stringed instrument.

# Student Guide
## Lesson 7. Optional: Your Vocal Cords

Causing the air in a wind instrument to vibrate produces a sound.

This lesson begins with your student feeling the vibrations coming from his throat as he recites the alphabet.

Then he moves on to think about how his vocal cords work when he speaks.

### Lesson Objectives

- Recognize that the sound of your voice is a result of your vocal cords vibrating.
- Describe how vocal cords produce sound as air passes through them.

---

# PREPARE

Approximate lesson time is 60 minutes.

### Materials

> For the Student
> Optional
>> tape recorder
>> yarn - 6 inch pieces (2)
>> containers, oatmeal
>> mirror
>> balloon
>> flashlight
>> rubber bands
>> household items - television

### Keywords and Pronunciation

**larynx** (LAIR-ingks)

**trachea** (TRAY-kee-uh)

**vocal cords** : Membranes in your throat that vibrate when air passes through them. This vibration is the first step in producing the sound of a voice. Your vocal cords vibrate when you speak.

**wind instrument** : An instrument in which air vibrates to make sound. A flute is a wind instrument.

---

# LEARN
## Activity 1. Optional: Optional Lesson Instructions *(Online)*

This lesson is OPTIONAL. It is provided for students who seek enrichment or extra practice. You may skip this lesson.

If you choose to skip this lesson, then go to the Plan or Lesson Lists page and mark this lesson "Skipped" in order to proceed to the next lesson in the course.

---

## Activity 2. Optional: Getting Ready to Make Noise *(Online)*

## Activity 3. Optional: Your Own Instrument *(Online)*

## Activity 4. Optional: Good Vibrations *(Online)*

## Activity 5. Optional: Review Your Vocal Cords *(Online)*

## Activity 6. Optional: See Your Voice *(Online)*

## Activity 7. Optional: International Voices *(Online)*

# *Student Guide*
## Lesson 8: Biography: Alexander Graham Bell

### Lesson Objectives

- Tell about the life and accomplishments of Alexander Graham Bell.
- Compare how telephones send and receive sounds with how humans send and receive sounds.
- Recognize that the sound of your voice is a result of your vocal cords vibrating.
- Identify the source of natural and man-made sounds.
- identify vibrating sources of sound.
- Demonstrate that sound waves travel through solids, liquids, and gases.
- Label the parts of the ear.
- Explain how sound is transmitted through the ear.
- Differentiate between pitch and volume.
- Demonstrate how to change the volume of a stringed instrument's sound.
- Recognize that the sound of your voice is a result of your vocal cords vibrating.
- Demonstrate mastery of the knowledge and skills taught in this unit.

# PREPARE

Approximate lesson time is 60 minutes.

### Advance Preparation

- Use a hammer and nail to punch one hole in the center of the bottom of two empty tin cans.

### Materials

  For the Student

  🖥 How a Telephone Works

  hammer

  nail - small

  can, tin - with hole in bottom (2)

  scissors, round-end safety

  string - 10-15 feet, waxed twine

# LEARN
## Activity 1: Long-Distance Communication *(Online)*

## Activity 2: Alexander Graham Bell *(Online)*

## Activity 3: How a Telephone Works *(Online)*

## Activity 4: The Whisper Phone *(Online)*
### Safety
Protect fingers and eyes when punching holes in the cans with the hammer and nail.

## Activity 5: Sounds Around Us Unit Review *(Online)*

---

# ASSESS
## Unit Assessment: Sounds Around Us (*Online*)
Your learning coach will help you complete an offline assessment covering the main objectives of this lesson. Your learning coach will score this assessment.

---

# LEARN
## Activity 6. Optional: Bell's Telephone *(Online)*

---

Name

Date

## How a Telephone Works

electric signal

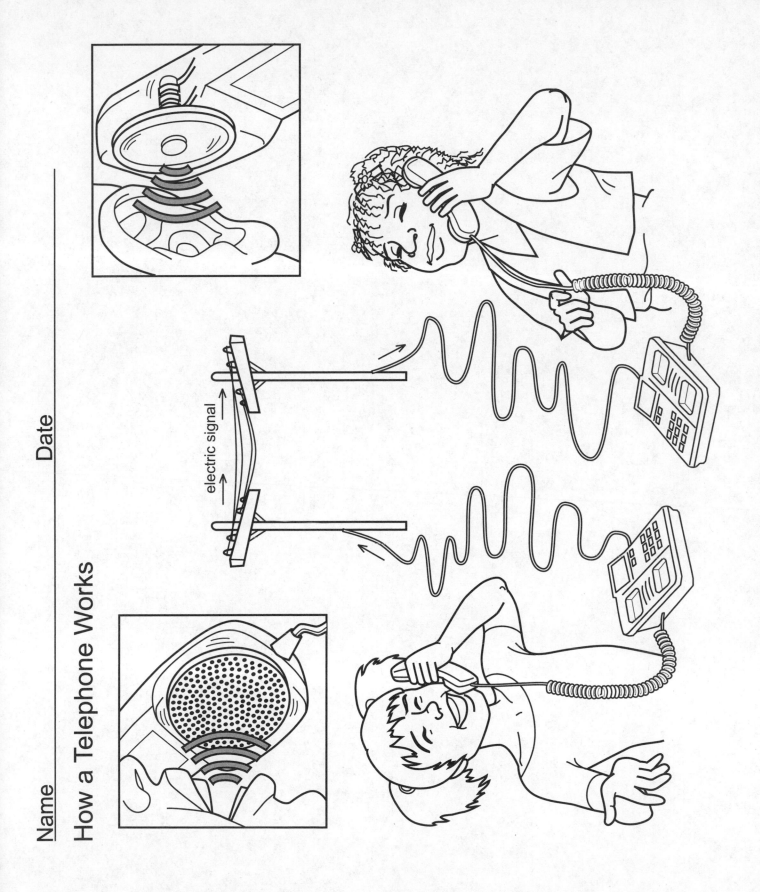

# Unit Assessment

## *Sounds Around Us*

1. Which of these sounds is man-made--a bird chirping or a police siren?

2. When you knock on a door, what vibrates and produces the sound you hear?

3. True or False: Sound travels only through gases, such as air, and never through liquids or solids.

4. Point to your outer ear flaps.

5. When sound waves travel into your ear, what part of your ear vibrates first--your eardrum or the tiny bones in your middle ear?

6. Imagine hitting a piece of metal forcefully, then softly. What changes--the volume or the pitch?

7. Which two words describe pitch--loud and soft or high and low?

8. If you wanted to make a very loud sound on a stringed instrument, like a guitar, would you pluck several different-sized strings or pluck the strings harder?

9. What happens to your vocal cords when air passes through them? Do they vibrate or do they block the flow of air?

10. Use your voice to make a low-pitched sound and a high-pitched sound.

# Student Guide
## Lesson 9: 1st Semester Assessment

## Lesson Objectives

- Demonstrate mastery of the knowledge and skills taught in this unit.
- Identify some common tools used by scientists for measuring, such as a balance, a graduated cylinder, a metric ruler, and a thermometer.
- Know that 100 centimeters equal 1 meter.
- Recognize that there are 1000mL in a liter.
- Measure volume in milliliters using a graduated cylinder.
- Know that moving heavy objects requires more force than moving light objects.
- Know that friction is a force that slows down or stops sliding objects.
- State that gravity pulls objects straight down to the Earth.
- Explain how machines make work easier.
- Identify different types of simple levers.
- Define the scientific term *work*.
- Explain that it takes less force to pull a load up an inclined plane than it does to lift the load to the same height.
- State that magnets have poles—areas of greatest magnetic strength.
- Demonstrate that magnets have two kinds of poles, and that similar poles repel and opposite poles attract.
- Explain how to make a temporary magnet.
- Explain that sound is made by vibrating objects.
- Explain how sound is transmitted through the ear.
- Differentiate between methods of changing volume and pitch on a stringed instrument.

---

# PREPARE

Approximate lesson time is 60 minutes.

## Advance Preparation

- In this lesson, your student will review the concepts he learned throughout the semester and will take the semester assessment. You may wish to collect his lab work or other activity sheets he has completed thus far to help him review for the assessment.

## Materials

For the Student

   📖 What Am I?

   scissors, round-end safety

Optional

   pencils, no. 2

---

# LEARN

## Activity 1: What Have We Done? *(Online)*

## Activity 2: What Am I? *(Online)*

Play What Am I? with your student.

Click to the next screen for instructions on how to play the game.

## Activity 3: Assessment Review *(Online)*

---

# ASSESS

## Semester Assessment: Science 2: 1st Semester Assessment (*Online*)

Complete an offline Semester Assessment. Your learning coach will score this part of the assessment.

---

# What Am I?

Read each card and guess what it describes.

cut

---

You use me to measure the amount of water in a glass. Am I a liter or a meter?

Liter

---

I am bigger than a centimeter. Am I a millimeter or a meter?

Meter

---

I am a scientific tool that measures how much space liquids take up or volume. Am I a spring scale or a graduated cylinder?

Graduated cylinder

---

I am a force, but don't be scared of me. I slow things down when they move. I am helpful to skydivers because I slow them down! Am I gravity or friction?

Friction

---

I am a force that pulls! If you drop something, I will pull it to the ground. When you jump, I pull you back to the ground, too.

Gravity

---

I like action! I am only performed when a force moves an object. But if there is no force and no object moving, you can't say I am there.

Work

---

I am a type of simple machine. You can make me with an arm and a fulcrum. You might have seen me as a seesaw at the playground. Am I a lever or a pulley?

Lever

---

I am a heavy overstuffed chair that needs to be put on a moving truck! Is it easier to lift me straight up or to walk me up a ramp?

Walk me up a ramp

---

# What Am I?

Read each card and guess what it describes.

cut

---

You can use me to make work easier. I can be a ramp, a lever, a wheel and axle, even a pulley! I am not complicated.

A simple machine

---

If you use a magnet to pick up paper clips, most of the clips will stick to me. Am I the middle of the magnet or am I the poles?

The poles

---

We are the north poles of two bar magnets. What happens if you place us together? Will the magnets attract or repel?

Repel

---

You can make me by rubbing a needle with a magnet several times in the same direction. But I won't stay magnetic forever.

A temporary magnet

---

I am a very thin piece of skin in your ear. When sound waves hit me, I vibrate!

Eardrum

---

If you change the thickness of guitar string, you will make me sound lower. Am I pitch or volume?

Pitch

---

You hear me whenever you strike something that vibrates. Any object that vibrates produces me.

---

When you speak, air passes across us and makes us vibrate. We are found in your throat.

---

# Semester Assessment

## *Science 2, Semester 1*

1. Which tool would you use to measure how much space a liquid takes up?

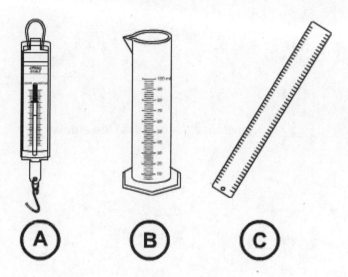

    Ⓐ        Ⓑ        Ⓒ

2. Which is greater in length--1 centimeter or 1 meter?

3. If you measured the amount of liquid in a glass, what units would you use--liters or centimeters?

4. Would more force be required to move a piano or a football?

5. Imagine that you drop a ball and it falls to the ground. What force causes the ball to fall?

6. Slide a pencil across the table. Which force slows and stops the pencil's movement--gravity or friction?

7. Which object is a lever--a seesaw or a bicycle wheel?

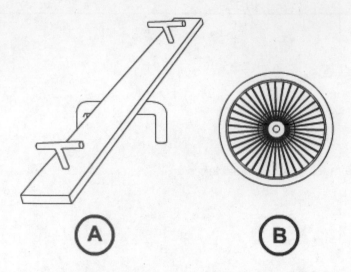

8. Machines make work easier because they _____ (increase or decrease) the amount of force needed to move an object.

9. Which worker is using more force?

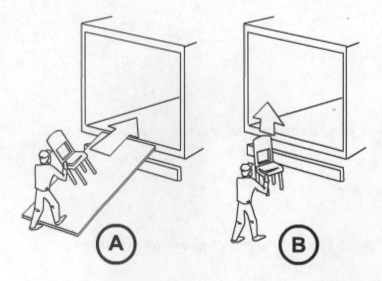

10. Which picture shows work being done?

11. Which set of magnets will repel each other?

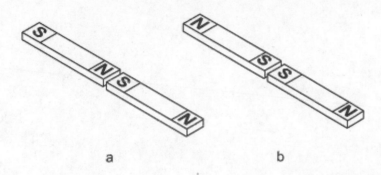

a                                    b

12. Where are bar magnets the strongest--in the middle or at the poles?

13. True or False: If you stroke a needle with a magnet several times in the same direction, you will make a temporary magnet.

14. True or False: Sound is produced by vibrating objects.

15. When sound waves enter your ear, they cause a thin skin called the _____ to vibrate.

16. Will changing the thickness of the string on a stringed instrument, such as a guitar, change its pitch or its volume?

# Answer Keys

# Lesson Assessment Answer Key

## *Meet the Metrics*

**Answers:**

1. balance, graduated cylinder, thermometer, metric ruler

2. You would use a balance to measure the mass of a baseball.

3. You would use a metric ruler to measure the length of a table.

4. A thermometer measures degrees Celsius.

5. A balance measures grams.

6. We use milliliters to measure volume.

Name _____ Date _____

# Lesson Assessment Answer Key

## *Why Does a Meter Matter?*

**Answers:**

**1.** the meter

**2.** 100

**3.** 1000

**4.** centimeters or millimeters

**5.** a meter stick, in units of meters

# Lesson Assessment Answer Key

## *Temperature Scales*

**Answers:**

**1.** degrees

**2.** Celsius

**3.** 100 degrees Celsius

**4.** 0 degrees on the Celsius scale and 32 degrees on the Fahrenheit scale

**5.** 37 degrees

# Lesson Assessment Answer Key

## *Let's Use a Liter*

**Answers:**

1. a graduated cylinder

2. 1000 milliliters

3. volume

# Lesson Assessment Answer Key

## *The Scientific Method*

**Answers:**

1. The question is the first step.

2. A possible explanation or prediction based on known information.

3. data

# Lesson Assessment Answer Key

## *Let's Measure Mass*

**Answers:**

1. A balance measures the mass of an object.

2. Your student measured mass using the balance.

3. There are 1000 grams in a kilogram.

4. Review your student's answers on the *What's Your Gold Worth sheet*. Answers will vary.

5. Review your student's answers on the *What's Your Gold Worth sheet*. Answers will vary.

# Unit Assessment Answer Key

## *Spring into Action*

**Answers:**

1. Degrees

2. 20 degrees Celsius

3. A

4. b. the graduated cylinder

5. milliliters

6. 1 liter

7. Centimeters

8. a. the balance

9. a bar graph

# Lesson Assessment Answer Key

## *Make It Move with Pushes and Pulls*

**Answers:**

1. A force is a push or a pull that can make an object move.

2. Accept any reasonable answer such as "using a force that is a push or pull."

3. The object changes position.

4. Make waves in the water.

5. The object will move toward you.

6. The object will move away from you.

# Lesson Assessment Answer Key

## *Measuring Pushes and Pulls*

**Answers:**

1. It takes more force to move a brick.

2. Your student should name the heaviest object. Often, the heaviest object is the harder to push or pull. However, some lighter objects may be harder to pull if you have to push or pull them across a rug or tabletop. For example, a shoe with a rubber sole may weigh less than a box, but pulling it across a table may take more force.

3. Yes. Often, the heaviest object is the harder to push or pull. However, some lighter objects may be harder to pull if you have put push or pull them across a rug or tabletop. For example, a shoe with a rubber sole may weigh less than a box, but pulling it across a table may take more force.

4. yes

# Lesson Assessment Answer Key

## *We've Got Friction*

**Answers:**

**1.** friction

**2.** Answers will vary but should refer to pulling the shoe across different surfaces.

**3.** Friction slows down or stops sliding objects.

# Lesson Assessment Answer Key

## *Groovy Gravity*

**Answers:**

1. Gravity

2. Your student should drop the ball and explain that gravity pulls the ball down to the ground.

3. Both objects hit the ground at the same time.

# Unit Assessment Answer Key

## *Balancing Act*

**Answers:**

1. force

2. c. the spring scale

3. Answers may vary but should include: dropping the object, pushing it off the table to let it drop, etc.

4. Both balls would touch the ground at the same time.

5. Friction

6. yes

# Lesson Assessment Answer Key

## *What Are Machines?*

**Answers:**

1. A force must act on an object and the object must move.

2. a lever

3. Answers may vary, but should include using a simple machine, like a lever.

4. machines, or simple machines

Name _____          Date _____

# Wheels and Axles Lab Sheet

## Part 1

Label the wheel and axle.

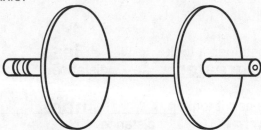

## Part 2

Make your predictions and record your observations.

**Question:**
Does lifting the container by turning the axle take more, less, or the same amount of work as lifting it by turning the wheels?

**Hypothesis:**
Lifting the container by turning the axle takes **MORE, LESS,** or **THE SAME AMOUNT OF** work as lifting it by turning the wheels. (Circle one)

**Procedure:**
1. Place a weight, such as a piece of fruit, into the container.
2. Stand next to a chair.
3. Turn the axle with your fingers to lift the container. Counting each natural turn of your fingers as one turn, determine the number of turns it takes to lift the container to the seat of the chair.
4. Unwind the string and lower the container to the floor.
5. Now turn the wheels with your hands to lift the container. Counting each natural turn of your hands as one turn, determine how many turns it takes to lift the container to the seat of the chair.

**Data:**
Did the load seem lighter when you lifted the container by turning the wheels or turning the axle?
**turning the wheels**

Name _____     Date _____

# Wheels and Axles Lab Sheet

# Part 3

Fill in the blanks with the words MORE or LESS (referring to force), GREATER or SHORTER (referring to distance), or THE SAME AMOUNT OF.

When you turned the wheels to lift the container, it took _____**less**_____ force, but you had to turn the wheels through a _____**greater**_____ distance.

When you turned the axle to lift the container, it took _____**more**_____ force, but you had to turn the axle through a _____**shorter**_____ distance.

The wheel turns **the same amount of** times while lifting the load.

No matter whether you turn the wheel or the axle, it takes **the same amount of** turns to lift the container.

# Lesson Assessment Answer Key

## *Wheels and Axles*

**Answers:**

1. a car tire

2. It would be easier to roll it on wheels. Wheels reduce friction by allowing objects to roll instead of slide.

3. LESS, GREATER

# Lesson Assessment Answer Key

## *Pulleys*

**Answers:**

**1.** arrow b

**2.** arrow a

**3.** a

**4.** b

**5.** up

**6.** a fixed pulley

# Lesson Assessment Answer Key

## *Inclined Planes, Wedges, and Screws*

**Answers:**

1. b. the one lifting the chair straight up

2. a. the one using the inclined plane

3. a wedge

4. an inclined plane

# Unit Assessment Answer Key

## *Machines Work Together*

1. Answers will vary but could include any example that demonstrates work (anything showing force being applied and object moving).

2. decrease

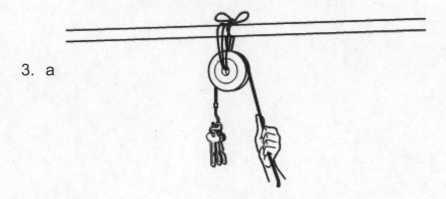

3. a

4. a car

5. the wheel's axle

6. b. a rope pulling an object using a grooved wheel

7. a wedge

8. b. the one lifiting the chair directly up

9. a lever

10. an inclined plane

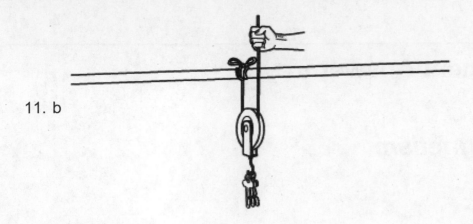

11. b

12. a pulley

13. a moveable pulley

14. a fixed pulley

# Lesson Assessment Answer Key

## *The Force of Magnetism*

**Answers:**

1. no
2. a nail
3. Answers will include horseshoe or U magnet, bar magnet, or ring magnet.
4. When the magnet is near the paper clips, they will appear to "jump" and attach themselves to the magnet.
5. The ends or poles picked up the most paper clips.

# Lesson Assessment Answer Key

## *Magnetic Poles and Fields*

**Answers:**

1. They repel, or push away from each other.
2. They attract, or pull toward each other.
3. Your student should draw the iron filings concentrated around the poles of the magnet.
4. at the poles
5. true

# Lesson Assessment Answer Key

## *Temporary Magnets*

**Answers:**

1. by stroking or rubbing it in one direction with a magnet
2. Because it is magnetic for a little while.
3. Answers may include that metal items are no longer attracted to it or that its molecules go back to the way they were before the object was magnetized.
4. iron or steel

# Unit Assessment Answer Key

## *Magnetism*

**Answers:**

1. A paper clip would be attracted to a magnet.
2. The poles of the magnet are strongest.
3. true
4. a. the magnets with opposite poles facing each other
5. a temporary magnet
6. field

# Lesson Assessment Answer Key

## *Sounds All Around*

**Answers:**

1. Answers may include wind, leaves rustling, twigs falling, and so forth.
2. Answers may include talking, laughing, snapping fingers, and so forth.
3. Answers may include a car horn, an ambulance siren, a street cleaner, and so forth.
4. Natural sounds may be people talking or a dog barking. Man-made sounds may include a phone ringing, a clock ticking, a radio playing, and so forth.

# Lesson Assessment Answer Key

## *Sound Waves*

**Answers:**

1. a plucked rubber band.
2. the object vibrates
3. the door and/or the doorjamb
4. the strings

# Lesson Assessment Answer Key

## *Sound Travels*

**Answers:**

1. yes
2. when you tapped the wood
3. air
4. when you tapped the bag of air

# Lesson Assessment Answer Key

## *The Ears Hear*

**Answers:**

1. The hammer, anvil, and stirrup are located in the middle ear.
2. true
3. the eardrum
4. cochlea
5. Possible answers may include two of the following: finding prey (food), hearing predators (other animals that hunt them for food), finding their way in the dark, or keeping cool.

# Lesson Assessment Answer Key

## *Exploring Pitch and Volume*

**Answers:**

1. its volume
2. low
3. a small bell
4. by striking the object with more force

# Lesson Assessment Answer Key

## *Musical Sound*

**Answers:**

1. tighten the strings
2. pluck the strings lightly
3. Answers will vary but should include changing the thickness, the length, and/or tightness of the strings.
4. Your student should pluck it strongly or lightly.

# Unit Assessment Answer Key

## *Sounds Around Us*

1. a police siren

2. the door and door jamb

3. false

4. Your student should point to the outer ear flaps on the sides of his head.

5. the eardrum

6. the volume

7. high and low

8. pluck the strings harder

9. they vibrate

10. Your student should be able to make a low-pitched sound and a high-pitched sound.

# Semester Assessment Answer Key

## *Science 2, Semester 1*

**Answers:**

1. B: graduated cylinder
2. 1 meter
3. liters
4. a piano
5. gravity
6. friction
7. A: a seesaw
8. Decrease
9. B: the worker lifting the chair into the truck
10. B: the picture of the weightlifter lifting the barbell.
11. B. the set with similar poles facing each other
12. at the poles
13. true
14. true
15. eardrum
16. its pitch